Knowing Me, Knowing You

A Multiple-Choice Quiz For Engaged Couples

The Woman's Quiz

Carol Brethour Stephens
Malcolm B. Stephens

Published by Counselor Press.

Counselor Press Website: www.counselorpress.com
Knowing Me, Knowing You Website: www.knowingme-knowingyou.com

ISBN 0-9746765-0-0

Dedicated to the glory of God
and to our dear, wonderful daughter Deanna

Table of Contents

Introduction

Every year many thousands of weddings take place and many thousands of divorces. The divorce trend is causing havoc in many people's lives, so we (the authors) have developed a quiz that helps couples to start their marriages with knowledge about each other and confidence in their expectations.

The sheer scope of what has been written about marriage is enormous. So what makes this book different? The quiz is accessible to all people—whatever their sex, race or education.

Perhaps the best way to define this book is by what it is not.

1. It is not open-ended. You do not have to list things you love about your fiancé, your personal strengths, or what type of tree you think you might be. Instead, because of the multiple-choice format, you simply pick the answer that best applies to you. The quiz is designed to be easy and fun, as well as informative.

2. It is not judgmental. Whether we like it or not, in our society, virtually every individual's view of right and wrong is different. It's important that each partner understand the other's perspective of right and wrong. The goal of the quiz is to reveal the values each partner holds.

3. It is not sexist. Frequently in any discussion of marriage, assumptions are made about the roles of men and women and the differences between them. Since these roles are in constant flux, the quiz for women and the one for men are almost identical; the range of traditional female and male responses is reflected in the possible answers, but other choices are possible.

4. It is not boring. The quiz helps you to focus in on your issues. You don't have to sit through a lengthy lecture on handling money if you and your partner are already in agreement. By pinpointing your personal issues, the quiz helps you concentrate on areas where you may have disagreements.

Reading Tips

Reading tips are listed in brief throughout the book, but the complete versions are described here. These tips help you to use the quiz in a way that will be most helpful for you and your fiancé.

Reading Tip #1 - There are two books for a very good reason. The quiz was designed so that you each fill it out on your own, without consulting your fiancé until you've finished each chapter or, if you prefer, the entire book. It is extremely important that you do your quiz separately from your partner. If you do it together, you may not feel free to voice your true opinion if your fiancé states his opinion first. Your perspective may be buried in a desire to be in harmony with him. The stronger personality will dominate! This is not true communication and will not benefit your relationship in the long run.

Reading Tip #2 - You can check off more than one answer per question. For example, under the question "When do you want children?" you may check off both "any time after I'm married" and "before I'm 40". Both answers might be true for you.

Reading Tip #3 - Be honest! First, you have to be honest with yourself; but don't worry, it's all laid out for you. What are your needs and expectations? In what areas do you fail to meet your own ideals? Self-examination can be hard to do, but before you can be honest with someone else, you need to be honest with yourself. Then, it is very important to be honest with your fiancé. If there are things you feel you can't reveal, when do you think that will change—in ten years or twenty? What if he finds out? Marriage that is based on anything less than honesty is automatically going to be tough going. Lack of trust or disillusionment can often lead to irreconcilable differences.

Reading Tip #4 - The quiz is designed to be non-judgmental, so relax. Although most of us have preconceived ideas of what is right and wrong, all that is necessary is for you and your fiancé to understand one another and agree. So, while some people might think it is disgraceful to, for example, cut yourself off from your family, you might have very good reasons for doing just that, and your fiancé may agree.

Reading Tip #5 - Make sure you and your fiancé agree about whether this quiz will be confidential and to what extent. Some of the material covered in this quiz is private. For example, some people might be uncomfortable discussing their sex lives or their history with drugs or alcohol. You have to agree whether you are going to share the information revealed in this quiz with anyone else. You may decide to discuss it with only a limited number of people (e.g. a minister conducting pre-marital counseling sessions).

Reading Tip #6 - Answer based on how you feel now, not how you think you'll feel in the future. Don't assume, for example, that if you can't stand children, that feeling will change as soon as you turn thirty-five. On the other hand, it is impossible to predict how we might react to circumstances that we've never experienced. A sudden loss of health or a rift in a family relationship can cause a shift in thinking. Since you can't know how you will feel ten years from now, all you can say is how you intend to act. Often our intentions guide our actions.

Reading Tip #7 - If your answer is not listed, write it in the margin. While we have tried to be comprehensive with our answers, every person is an individual. Consequently, if you come up with an answer that is not listed, feel free to write it in the margin. The purpose of the quiz is to get you thinking about issues that come up in marriage. It is our hope that this will lead to an even deeper understanding between you and your fiancé.

Reading Tip #8 - After you've finished a chapter (or the whole book), compare your answers with your fiancé's. This is linked to Reading Tip #1.

Reading Tip #9 - Highlight those questions to which you and your fiancé gave very different answers. These are the issues that you need to discuss in more depth.

Reading Tip #10 - This quiz helps you pinpoint your personal issues as a couple; you need to decide how to respond. This book does not advise you about what to do. It provides you with knowledge of one another. When you are in conflict on a given issue, you have a choice. You can work out your differences (e.g. compromise with each other). You can promise each other ahead of time that you can live with those differences for the rest of your lives. In some rare cases, you may discover before it's too late that the fundamental differences are so great that a life together would be filled with conflict and misery. We don't propose those solutions. The choice is up to you.

Reading Tip #11 - If your fiancé won't do the man's quiz, still go through your quiz on your own. Really good relationships are based on a certain amount of self-knowledge. If you can begin to become aware of what makes you tick or what things you really can't stand, then you are in a better position to judge your relationship. You may even be able to raise some of the questions casually with your fiancé.

Chapter 1

Household Chores

Case Study

Diane was a born neat freak. When she married Glen, they agreed to split the household cleaning since they were both working at full-time jobs. However, she expected him to keep to her standard of cleanliness, which included vacuuming every day. "When I agreed vacuuming would be my job, I thought we would do it once a week like normal people," he roared one day after she caught him skipping his duties. "I'll do it once a week. If you want it done the other days, you can do it yourself."

QUIZ

1. How important is it to you that your home be clean (e.g. free from mud and dust)?
   - ☐ extremely important
   - ☐ reasonably important
   - ☐ important
   - ☐ not very important
   - ☐ not at all important

2. How important is it to you that your home be very tidy?
   - ☐ extremely important
   - ☐ reasonably important
   - ☐ important
   - ☐ not very important
   - ☐ not at all important

3. Do you ever leave clothes lying on the floor?
   - ☐ always
   - ☐ sometimes
   - ☐ rarely
   - ☐ never

4. Do crumbs on the kitchen counter bother you?
   - ☐ yes
   - ☐ sometimes
   - ☐ no

5. Do you like to keep mementos (some people refer to it as being a pack rat)?
   - ☐ yes, a lot
   - ☐ yes, if it's important (i.e. a special occasion)
   - ☐ yes, but I just keep photographs
   - ☐ no, not usually
   - ☐ no, never

6. Do you have a hobby that requires space and can't be put away (e.g. picture puzzles, woodworking, sewing)?
   - ☐ yes
   - ☐ no
   - ☐ sometimes

7. How would you feel if your husband had such a hobby?
   - ☐ I'd be happy that he has something he enjoys
   - ☐ as long as it was in a separate workshop or room, it would be okay
   - ☐ once in a while it would be okay, but not constantly
   - ☐ I wouldn't be able to stand the mess in the house

8. Do you regularly go through your home to throw things away?
   - ☐ no, I live with my parents or roommates
   - ☐ yes, once every few months
   - ☐ yes, once a year
   - ☐ rarely
   - ☐ never

9. Do you believe in doing major spring-cleaning?
   - ☐ yes, every year
   - ☐ yes; not every year, but every other year
   - ☐ yes, every few years
   - ☐ no

Reading Tip

Fill out the quiz on your own, without consulting your fiancé until you've finished each chapter. For more reading tips, see the Introduction.

10. Who do you think should be responsible for spring-cleaning?
    - ☐ I will be
    - ☐ my husband will be
    - ☐ whoever is the least busy (with work, not recreational activities) will do it
    - ☐ whoever is most concerned about cleanliness will do it
    - ☐ we'll contract someone to do it
    - ☐ we'll do it together
    - ☐ we'll take turns

11. Who do you think should be responsible for decorating your home?
    - ☐ I will be
    - ☐ my husband will be
    - ☐ whoever is the least busy with work will do it
    - ☐ whoever is most concerned about the appearance of the house will do it
    - ☐ an interior decorator will do it
    - ☐ a family member (e.g. parents who give furniture) will do it
    - ☐ we'll do it together

12. Do you think of the kitchen as the woman's domain?
    - ☐ yes
    - ☐ no

13. Who do you think should do the cooking?
    - ☐ me
    - ☐ my husband
    - ☐ whoever is better at it
    - ☐ whoever is the least busy with work
    - ☐ someone else (e.g. we'll eat out a lot)
    - ☐ we'll take turns
    - ☐ we'll do it together

14. Who do you think should put out the trash?
    - ☐ me
    - ☐ my husband
    - ☐ whoever is the least busy with work
    - ☐ whoever finds the trash-can full
    - ☐ we'll take turns

15. Who do you think should do the dishes or load the dishwasher?
    - ☐ me
    - ☐ my husband
    - ☐ whoever is the least busy with work
    - ☐ whoever can't stand an untidy kitchen
    - ☐ whoever uses the last dish
    - ☐ we'll hire a maid
    - ☐ we'll take turns
    - ☐ we'll do it together

16. How often should the dishes be done?
    - ☐ 2 or 3 times a day
    - ☐ every day
    - ☐ whenever we have company coming over
    - ☐ whenever we have time
    - ☐ whenever we run out of dishes
    - ☐ we'll use paper plates

17. Who do you think should do the dusting?
    - ☐ me
    - ☐ my husband
    - ☐ whoever is the least busy with work
    - ☐ whoever dislikes a dusty house the most
    - ☐ we'll hire a maid
    - ☐ we'll take turns
    - ☐ we'll do it together

18. How often should the dusting be done?
    - ☐ every day
    - ☐ once or twice a week
    - ☐ once a month
    - ☐ whenever we have company coming over
    - ☐ whenever we have time
    - ☐ whenever we notice a lot of dust

19. Who do you think should do the vacuuming?
    - ☐ me
    - ☐ my husband
    - ☐ whoever is the least busy with work
    - ☐ whoever dislikes a dirty carpet the most
    - ☐ we'll hire a maid
    - ☐ we'll take turns

20. How often should the vacuuming be done?
    - ☐ every day
    - ☐ once or twice a week
    - ☐ once or twice a month
    - ☐ whenever we have company coming over
    - ☐ whenever we have time
    - ☐ whenever we notice the carpets need it

21. Do you think the beds need to be made every day?
    - ☐ yes, definitely
    - ☐ yes, if we have time
    - ☐ it would be nice, but not absolutely necessary
    - ☐ I don't care if the bed is made or not

22. Who do you think should be responsible for making the bed?
    - ☐ I will be
    - ☐ my husband will be
    - ☐ whoever is the least busy with work will do it
    - ☐ whoever can't stand an unmade bed will do it
    - ☐ the bed doesn't need to be made
    - ☐ we'll hire a maid to make the bed
    - ☐ we'll take turns
    - ☐ we'll do it together

23. Who do you think should be responsible for cleaning the toilets?
    - ☐ I will be
    - ☐ my husband will be
    - ☐ whoever is the least busy with work will do it
    - ☐ whoever can't stand a disgusting toilet will do it
    - ☐ we'll hire a maid
    - ☐ we'll take turns

24. Who do you think should be responsible for cleaning the bathtub/shower and sinks?
    - ☐ I will be
    - ☐ my husband will be
    - ☐ whoever is the least busy with work will do it
    - ☐ whoever can't stand dirty sinks or bathtubs will do it
    - ☐ whoever has the most showers or baths will do it
    - ☐ we'll hire a maid
    - ☐ we'll take turns
    - ☐ we'll do it together

25. How often should the bathroom be cleaned?
    - ☐ every day
    - ☐ once a week
    - ☐ once or twice a month
    - ☐ whenever we have company coming over
    - ☐ whenever we have time
    - ☐ whenever we see something disgusting growing in there

26. Who do you think should be responsible for doing the laundry?
    - ☐ I will be
    - ☐ my husband will be
    - ☐ whoever is the least busy with work will do it
    - ☐ whoever runs out of clean clothes first will do it
    - ☐ we'll each launder our own clothes and take turns doing the household laundry (e.g. sheets, towels)
    - ☐ we'll take turns doing all the laundry
    - ☐ we'll do it together
    - ☐ other ______________________________

27. Who do you think should be responsible for cleaning the basement?
    - ☐ I will be
    - ☐ my husband will be
    - ☐ whoever is the least busy with work will do it
    - ☐ whoever is most concerned about it will do it
    - ☐ we'll contract someone to do it
    - ☐ we'll take turns
    - ☐ we'll do it together
    - ☐ we won't have a basement

28. Who do you think should be responsible for household repairs (e.g. fixing a dripping faucet, painting)?
    - ☐ I will be
    - ☐ my husband will be
    - ☐ whoever is the least busy with work will do it
    - ☐ whoever is most concerned about the appearance and functionality of the house will do it
    - ☐ whoever is better at the task (e.g. steady hands are required for painting) will do it
    - ☐ we'll contract someone to do it
    - ☐ we'll do it together

29. Who do you think should be responsible for home improvements (e.g. adding a deck or finishing the basement)?
    - ☐ I will be
    - ☐ my husband will be
    - ☐ whoever is the least busy with work will do it
    - ☐ whoever wants the work done will do it
    - ☐ whoever is better at that type of work will do it
    - ☐ we'll contract someone to do it
    - ☐ we'll do it together

30. Do you think of the garage as the husband's domain?
    - ☐ yes
    - ☐ no
    - ☐ I don't know

31. Who do you think should be responsible for cleaning the garage?
    - ☐ I will be
    - ☐ my husband will be
    - ☐ whoever is the least busy with work will do it
    - ☐ whoever is most concerned about it will do it
    - ☐ we'll contract someone to do it
    - ☐ we'll take turns
    - ☐ we'll do it together
    - ☐ we won't have a garage

32. Who do you think should be responsible for cutting the lawn?
    - ☐ I will be
    - ☐ my husband will be
    - ☐ whoever is the least busy with work will do it
    - ☐ whoever is embarrassed by a messy yard will do it
    - ☐ we'll contract someone to do it
    - ☐ we'll take turns
    - ☐ we won't have a lawn

33. How often do you think the lawn needs cutting?
    - ☐ twice a week
    - ☐ once a week
    - ☐ whenever it looks long (i.e. 5 or more inches)
    - ☐ once a month

34. Who do you think should be responsible for tending the flower gardens?
    - ☐ I will be
    - ☐ my husband will be
    - ☐ whoever is the least busy with work will do it
    - ☐ whoever is most concerned about the look of our property will do it
    - ☐ we'll contract someone to do it
    - ☐ we'll take turns
    - ☐ we'll do it together
    - ☐ we won't have flower gardens

35. Who do you think should shovel snow?
    - ☐ me
    - ☐ my husband
    - ☐ whoever is the least busy with work
    - ☐ we'll contract someone to do it
    - ☐ we'll take turns
    - ☐ we'll do it together
    - ☐ it doesn't snow where we'll be living

36. When should the snow be shoveled?
    - ☐ when it is 2" deep
    - ☐ when it is 6" deep
    - ☐ when we have time
    - ☐ when we can't drive over it anymore without getting stuck

37. Who will be responsible for killing bugs or catching mice?
    - ☐ I will be
    - ☐ my husband will be
    - ☐ whoever sees the creature first will take care of it
    - ☐ we'll contract someone to do it
    - ☐ we'll get a pet to take care of it (e.g. cats eat mice)

38. If you have a pet, who will be responsible for it?
    - ☐ I will be
    - ☐ my husband will be
    - ☐ whoever is the least busy with work will take care of it
    - ☐ whoever wanted the pet will take care of it
    - ☐ we'll do it together
    - ☐ we'll take turns

Chapter 2

Compatibility

Case Study

Before they were married, Nigel and Ellen were both sports nuts. Nigel played golf, and Ellen competed in figure skating. After they were married and parents, however, Ellen had to drop skating to care for their children. Nigel still spent all weekend on the golf course, and spent one week a year on a golf trip with his buddies. "The kids are growing up without you," Ellen complained. "Your golf buddies see you more than I do. It's not right!"

QUIZ

1. How do you define romantic love?
   - ☐ a strong sexual attraction—my heart beats faster when he comes near
   - ☐ an abiding sense of warmth—I long to be near him
   - ☐ a feeling of trust
   - ☐ a sexual attraction that is based on the special qualities of my fiancé
   - ☐ a sexual attraction that needs to be nurtured by a continuing loving relationship
   - ☐ a feeling that I can't live without him
   - ☐ a choice to fall deeply in love with a man I respect, admire and like, as well as love
   - ☐ other ______________________________

2. What do you think is <u>the</u> most important aspect of marriage (pick one)?
   - ☐ love
   - ☐ sex
   - ☐ communication
   - ☐ co-operation
   - ☐ trust
   - ☐ respect
   - ☐ sharing of responsibilities
   - ☐ laughing together
   - ☐ forgiving each other
   - ☐ faith in God
   - ☐ common goals and interests
   - ☐ children
   - ☐ other ____________________

Reading Tip

You can check off more than one answer per question. See the Introduction for more reading tips.

3. In order of importance in the marriage, how would you rank the following (1 being the most important)?

	Rank
☐ love	____
☐ sex	____
☐ communication	____
☐ co-operation	____
☐ trust	____
☐ respect	____
☐ sharing of responsibilities	____
☐ laughing together	____
☐ forgiving each other	____
☐ faith in God	____
☐ common goals and interests	____
☐ children	____
☐ other ____________________	____

4. What are your life goals? Cross out any that don't apply and rank the rest in order of importance (1 being the most important).

	Rank
☐ raising a family	____
☐ sending my children to college	____
☐ making a fortune	____
☐ climbing the corporate ladder	____
☐ being proficient at my work and recognized for it	____
☐ exploring my special talents	____
☐ buying my own home	____
☐ having enough money to retire	____
☐ serving God	____
☐ serving my country	____
☐ helping other people (e.g. public service)	____
☐ doing my best at everything I do	____
☐ travelling	____
☐ finding myself	____
☐ being happy	____
☐ other ______________________________	____

5. When you and your fiancé disagree about what decision to make (e.g. when picking a house), how do you plan to handle the disagreement?
   - ☐ whoever feels more strongly about the decision gets his/her way
   - ☐ whoever wears the other one down gets his/her way
   - ☐ if we can't agree, we won't do anything (the authors call this a veto)
   - ☐ my husband will make the final decision
   - ☐ I will make the final decision
   - ☐ we'll flip a coin

6. What would be your dream home?
   - ☐ a luxury high-rise condo
   - ☐ a mansion
   - ☐ a home in a gorgeous, gated community
   - ☐ a home in a golf-course community
   - ☐ a nice little house with a picket fence
   - ☐ a grand, old, century home
   - ☐ a house in the country
   - ☐ a farm
   - ☐ a trailer
   - ☐ a mobile home
   - ☐ the house I grew up in
   - ☐ other ______________________________

7. If you were to go on your dream vacation, what would it be?
   - ☐ relaxing in some tropical paradise, sipping a cold drink
   - ☐ biking or hiking through the Grand Canyon or over the Swiss Alps
   - ☐ visiting destinations that are important historically
   - ☐ visiting exotic (maybe dangerous) foreign places, just for the experience
   - ☐ dirt biking through rugged areas
   - ☐ taking a motorcycle trip wherever the road takes us
   - ☐ camping near home
   - ☐ going to a cottage
   - ☐ traveling through our country in an RV (motorhome)
   - ☐ visiting a working ranch and joining in
   - ☐ going to Disney World
   - ☐ staying in five-star hotels (it doesn't matter where)
   - ☐ cruising
   - ☐ staying home
   - ☐ other ______________________________

8. Do you expect to vacation with your husband?
   - ☐ always
   - ☐ sometimes separate vacations would be okay
   - ☐ sometimes I'll go on a separate vacation with friends or family
   - ☐ we'll vacation together, but with other people (e.g. family or friends)
   - ☐ I don't expect to vacation with my husband

9. Do you and your fiancé share any interests (e.g. sports, involvement in church, hobbies)?
   - ☐ yes
   - ☐ no

10. How many interests do you share? If you want to, name them.
    - ☐ 1 – 3
    - ☐ 3 – 5
    - ☐ 5 – 10
    - ☐ 10+

11. If your fiancé has a hobby or interest that you don't share, how do you feel about him spending time at this activity?
    - ☐ I'm okay with it and I'll share it for his sake
    - ☐ I'll try it with an open mind to see if I like it
    - ☐ I'm okay with it as long as I don't have to participate
    - ☐ it's okay for now, but when we have children, I'll expect his priorities to change
    - ☐ I have my own interests that he won't engage in, so it's fair
    - ☐ I don't particularly want this hobby or interest to take up a lot of his time
    - ☐ I resent the time this hobby or interest takes

12. When you are playing a game or sport against a friend, is it really important to you to win?
    - ☐ yes, that's why I play—for the challenge and the thrill
    - ☐ yes, I like winning
    - ☐ it would be nice to win, but I'm not devastated if I lose
    - ☐ I don't really care whether I win or not

13. When you are playing a game or sport where your fiancé is your opponent, do you feel the same way?
    - ☐ yes
    - ☐ sometimes
    - ☐ no (e.g. even if I'm strongly competitive, I'm happy for him if he wins)

14. How do you handle winning or losing a game or sport?
    - ☐ I don't care so I don't act any particular way
    - ☐ if I lose, I congratulate the victor
    - ☐ if I lose, I get angry
    - ☐ if I lose, I mope
    - ☐ if I lose, I insult the winner (e.g. I say things like "You got lucky this time")
    - ☐ if I win, I insult the loser (e.g. I say things like "In your face")

15. If you and your fiancé are on the same team competing against someone else, how do you treat him?
    - ☐ I play for fun, so we laugh together
    - ☐ I encourage him to do his best
    - ☐ I get annoyed if he misses a chance to score
    - ☐ I snap at him to shape up if he doesn't do well

16. Do you and your fiancé find the same things funny?
    - ☐ yes
    - ☐ most of the time
    - ☐ some of the time
    - ☐ no
    - ☐ his sense of humor irritates me

17. Do you laugh when you're in one another's company?
    - ☐ yes
    - ☐ a lot of the time
    - ☐ some of the time
    - ☐ no

18. Do you like the same movies or TV shows?
    - ☐ yes
    - ☐ most of the time
    - ☐ some of the time
    - ☐ no

19. If you both like different shows, which shows will you both watch?
    - ☐ all the shows we each like (we'll videotape if two are on at once)
    - ☐ we'll watch primarily what my fiancé likes to watch
    - ☐ we'll watch primarily what I like to watch
    - ☐ we'll only watch what we both enjoy and save the other shows for when each of us is alone
    - ☐ we'll watch TV separately

20. Do you want a pet and, if so, what type?
    - ☐ no, I don't want any pets
    - ☐ yes, I don't care what type
    - ☐ yes, I want all sorts of different pets
    - ☐ yes, I love dogs
    - ☐ yes, I love cats
    - ☐ yes, I love birds
    - ☐ yes, I love reptiles
    - ☐ yes, I love spiders (e.g. tarantulas)
    - ☐ yes, I love guinea pigs, mice, etc.
    - ☐ yes, other ________________________

21. Are there things at which your fiancé excels which you either are not good at or dislike doing (i.e. you complement each other)? For example, one of you might not drive, but is a great map-reader. The other might be a good driver, but be hopeless with maps.
    - ☐ yes
    - ☐ no

22. In how many areas do you complement one another (complement is defined in the previous question and should not be confused with compliment—to say something nice)?
    - ☐ 1 – 2
    - ☐ 3 – 5
    - ☐ 5 – 10
    - ☐ 10+

23. How would you feel if your husband was able to take on a task that you personally dislike (e.g. cooking, finances)?
    - ☐ it would be wonderful; what a relief
    - ☐ it would be good
    - ☐ I'd think that he was infringing on my territory, even though I'm not good with this task

24. Once you're married, which of the following bad habits would you find most difficult to live with (limit yourself to five to start)?
    - ☐ passing wind
    - ☐ burping loudly in public
    - ☐ picking his teeth in public
    - ☐ scratching himself in public
    - ☐ spitting for sport
    - ☐ picking his nose
    - ☐ chewing his fingernails
    - ☐ cutting his nails in bed
    - ☐ leaving nail clippings around
    - ☐ leaving underwear and/or dirty clothes on the floor
    - ☐ squeezing toothpaste in the middle instead of at the end
    - ☐ leaving the tops off bottles in the shower
    - ☐ leaving the toilet seat up
    - ☐ leaving whiskers in the sink after shaving
    - ☐ not replacing toilet paper or paper towels that have run out
    - ☐ putting toilet paper on backwards
    - ☐ leaving towels on the floor
    - ☐ not washing his hands after going to the bathroom or getting dirty
    - ☐ drinking directly from the milk (or orange juice) carton
    - ☐ putting empty containers back in the fridge
    - ☐ drinking directly from the faucet
    - ☐ leaving cupboard doors open
    - ☐ snoring
    - ☐ stealing pillows and covers while sleeping
    - ☐ waking me up in the middle of the night to talk
    - ☐ waking me up in the middle of the night for sex
    - ☐ waking me up from a sound sleep by being inconsiderate (e.g. using power tools or vacuuming)
    - ☐ tracking mud through the house
    - ☐ constantly jiggling his legs
    - ☐ leaving used tissues lying about
    - ☐ not cleaning up after himself
    - ☐ undoing his belt in public and hitching up his pants
    - ☐ not wearing a shirt in public
    - ☐ sitting around in underwear
    - ☐ spending too much time on the phone
    - ☐ not being able to get off the phone
    - ☐ spending too much time on the computer
    - ☐ ignoring me
    - ☐ always being late

… continued

□ telling the same stories over and over
□ reading the newspaper over my shoulder
□ other ______________________________

25. In order to make you completely happy and satisfied, how much would your husband have to change?
□ a lot—some of his characteristics drive me crazy
□ some—he has to be willing to meet me half way
□ a little—I like him basically just as he is
□ not at all

26. If you want him to change, do you think that will happen once you're married?
□ yes
□ no
□ I hope so
□ I don't know

Chapter 3

Sex

Case Study

Juan and Sophie had been married for five years, and enjoyed a great love life. Juan was so romantic, and they often made love three times a week. They decided to start a family. Two months into the pregnancy, after an evening of lovemaking, Sophie experienced cramps and spotting. The obstetrician explained that the pregnancy was at risk and sex might cause a miscarriage. They were to abstain from lovemaking until after the baby was delivered. Sophie was worried and resigned, but Juan was horrified. Seven months without sex! He wasn't sure he could manage!

QUIZ

1. Do you believe in sex before marriage?
   - ☐ yes
   - ☐ yes, if we really love each other
   - ☐ yes, as long as we are committed to one another
   - ☐ no

2. If no, do you expect your fiancé to respect your desire to save sex for marriage?
   - ☐ yes
   - ☐ no

3. Do you expect your husband to be a virgin?
   - ☐ yes
   - ☐ no
   - ☐ I don't want to know

4. If you believe sex before marriage is okay and you have previous sexual experience, would you be willing to be tested for communicable diseases?
   - □ yes
   - □ no

> **Reading Tip**
>
> This quiz is designed to be non-judgmental, so relax. For more reading tips, see the Introduction.

5. How important do you think sex will be in your marriage?
   - □ it will be the most important aspect of marriage
   - □ it will be very important
   - □ it will be somewhat important
   - □ it will not be terribly important
   - □ it will not be at all important
   - □ it will be a special bond between us

6. In a marriage relationship, who do you think should initiate sex?
   - □ husband
   - □ wife
   - □ either partner

7. Do you think sex is a marital right to automatically be given to the other when suggested?
   - □ yes
   - □ no

8. If no, under what conditions would it be okay to say no to sex?
   - □ if we've just had a fight
   - □ if one of us is in poor health
   - □ if one of us is in pain
   - □ if I was nine months pregnant
   - □ if we've just had a baby
   - □ if one of us is lacking sleep
   - □ if I don't feel like it
   - □ if my husband doesn't feel like it

9. How often would you <u>like</u> to make love in a perfect world?
   - □ several times a day
   - □ once a day
   - □ twice a week
   - □ once a week
   - □ twice a month
   - □ once a month
   - □ less frequently

10. Realistically, knowing your commitments to jobs, family and other responsibilities, how often do you expect to make love?
    - ☐ several times a day
    - ☐ once a day
    - ☐ twice a week
    - ☐ once a week
    - ☐ twice a month
    - ☐ once a month
    - ☐ less frequently

11. Are you comfortable with the thought of being naked in front of your spouse?
    - ☐ yes
    - ☐ no
    - ☐ I'm not sure

12. What conditions would be <u>unacceptable</u> to you when making love?
    - ☐ if we lacked privacy
    - ☐ if it is daylight or the lights are on
    - ☐ if we're not in a bed
    - ☐ if we're in a public place
    - ☐ if we're staying at my parent's or my in-law's homes
    - ☐ other ______________________________

13. Are there any sexual acts which you would be unwilling to do?
    - ☐ none
    - ☐ I would not want to make lots of noise
    - ☐ I would not be comfortable with foreplay
    - ☐ I may not like certain positions (e.g. if they are painful)
    - ☐ I would not like oral sex
    - ☐ I would be uncomfortable with role-playing
    - ☐ I would not want my husband fantasizing that I am someone else
    - ☐ I would not want to fantasize about someone other than my husband
    - ☐ other ______________________________

14. Would you feel free to tell your husband what you like and dislike during sex?
    - ☐ yes
    - ☐ probably
    - ☐ probably not
    - ☐ no

15. If your husband told you what he likes and dislikes during sex, how would you react?
    - ☐ I'd say "great", and try to please him
    - ☐ I'd be okay with it
    - ☐ I'd be upset if there was something he didn't like
    - ☐ I'd feel like a poor lover
    - ☐ I'd retaliate and tell him things that he does that I don't like
    - ☐ I'd ignore his comments
    - ☐ I'd be uncomfortable talking about it

16. In your mind, would you ever compare your spouse to a past lover (if you had one)?
    - ☐ definitely
    - ☐ probably
    - ☐ I'd try not to
    - ☐ I wouldn't

17. Would you ever tell your husband how he compares to a past lover?
    - ☐ yes
    - ☐ possibly, if I was very angry
    - ☐ no
    - ☐ only if it was a favorable comparison

18. Do you plan to talk to others about your sex life?
    - ☐ no, it is private between me and my husband
    - ☐ yes, with family
    - ☐ yes, with friends
    - ☐ yes, with a doctor or counselor

19. Are you in favor of contraceptives?
    - ☐ yes
    - ☐ no
    - ☐ I'm not sure

20. If no, why?
    - ☐ they are bad for my health or my husband's health
    - ☐ I am morally opposed to contraceptives
    - ☐ I want a large family
    - ☐ other ______________________________

21. If you plan to use a contraceptive, what type would you and your husband use?
    - ☐ the pill
    - ☐ condom
    - ☐ spermicide
    - ☐ sponge
    - ☐ diaphragm
    - ☐ vasectomy
    - ☐ tubal ligation (i.e. when a woman gets her tubes tied)
    - ☐ other ______________________________
    - ☐ none

22. Do you think that contraceptives are 100% reliable?
    - ☐ yes
    - ☐ no

23. What would you do if the doctor says that sex is not recommended for a specified period of time (e.g. difficult pregnancy, recovery from a heart attack)?
    - ☐ I'd wait patiently
    - ☐ I'd take cold showers
    - ☐ I'd pressure my spouse to take a chance
    - ☐ I'd find other ways of being intimate with my husband
    - ☐ I'd watch sexy movies or read sexy books
    - ☐ I'd masturbate
    - ☐ I'd start showing interest in men other than my husband
    - ☐ I'd have an affair
    - ☐ other ______________________________

24. What positions do you favor when making love?
    - ☐ I don't know yet
    - ☐ top
    - ☐ bottom
    - ☐ lying side by side facing one another
    - ☐ sitting
    - ☐ standing
    - ☐ other ______________________________
    - ☐ I don't care

25. Do you believe in sexual fidelity?
    - ☐ yes
    - ☐ no
    - ☐ most of the time

26. Under what circumstances might it be okay to be sexually unfaithful?
    - ☐ never
    - ☐ if my husband is unavailable to have sex
    - ☐ if my husband is unwilling to have sex for a specified period of time or less frequently than I'd like
    - ☐ if I fall out of love with my husband
    - ☐ if I fall in love with someone else
    - ☐ if I'm bored
    - ☐ other ____________________

27. Have you read or watched explicitly sexual material?
    - ☐ yes
    - ☐ no

28. If yes, what form of "entertainment" has this been?
    - ☐ a strip club
    - ☐ an X-rated movie
    - ☐ sexy books
    - ☐ Playgirl magazine
    - ☐ pornography
    - ☐ sites on the internet
    - ☐ other ____________________

29. Is this something you do frequently (e.g. once a month or more)?
    - ☐ yes
    - ☐ no

30. If yes, will you continue to do so when you're married?
    - ☐ yes
    - ☐ no
    - ☐ we'll do it together

Chapter 4

Communication

Case Study

Jim's parents had a happy marriage, but they rarely spoke except about the news. Nevertheless, they showed their love by always holding hands and cuddling, even in public. This had caused him no end of embarrassment during his teen years. After he married Elaine, he was equally attentive physically and still felt very much in love. He was shocked when he overheard Elaine tell her mother that she wasn't sure that he still loved her, because he never told her so.

QUIZ

1. How would you describe yourself?
   - ☐ outgoing, friendly, open about my feelings
   - ☐ friendly, but not open about my feelings
   - ☐ shy, reserved
   - ☐ shy until I get to know someone and then I'm quite open about how I feel
   - ☐ formal, proper, constrained
   - ☐ other ______________________________

2. Which one of the following makes you feel the <u>most</u> loved (loosely adapted from the book *The Five Love Languages* by Gary Chapman, 1992)?
   - ☐ when I'm touched lovingly (e.g. when my fiancé strokes my hair or gives me a hug)
   - ☐ when my fiancé tells me "I love you" or says something else good about me (e.g. "You look great")
   - ☐ when my fiancé shares my chores or does something nice for me
   - ☐ when my fiancé spends quality time with me
   - ☐ when my fiancé gives me gifts (e.g. chocolates)

3. Rank the following in order of importance to you (1 being the most important).

	Rank
☐ when I'm touched lovingly (as in the previous question)	____
☐ when my fiancé says "I love you" or says something else good about me	____
☐ when my fiancé shares my chores or does something nice for me	____
☐ when my fiancé spends quality time with me	____
☐ when my fiancé gives me gifts (e.g. chocolates)	____

4. How do you intend to communicate with your husband when you're married?
   - ☐ I'll say something once and expect him to remember it
   - ☐ I'll expect my husband to listen to me, even though I talk a lot
   - ☐ I'll talk in detail to make sure he knows everything that happened to me on a given day
   - ☐ I'll repeat myself several times, just to make sure he gets it
   - ☐ I'll set aside some time every day to talk with my husband
   - ☐ I'm not really a talker, so I'll discourage conversation
   - ☐ I'll grunt
   - ☐ I'll use my tone of voice more than my actual words as a way of communicating my feelings (but not my thoughts)
   - ☐ I'll give my husband non-verbal cues about how I feel (e.g. I'll give him tickets to his favorite sporting event as a way of saying "I'm sorry" or "I love you")
   - ☐ other ____

Reading Tip

Be honest! For more reading tips, see the Introduction.

5. What will you do if your husband's communication style is different than yours?
   - ☐ I'll adjust to his style
   - ☐ I'll ignore how he feels and insist he communicate like I do
   - ☐ we will probably have trouble communicating because neither of us wants to change style
   - ☐ we'll try to negotiate a compromise that will be the best way for us to communicate

6. When will you communicate about important issues (e.g. parenting, upsetting news, problems at work)?
   - ☐ we'll make sure we eat together every night and discuss things over dinner
   - ☐ just before bed, we'll make time to talk
   - ☐ we'll try to grab time over breakfast to discuss issues
   - ☐ we'll talk about them wherever we happen to be together (e.g. grocery store, the car)
   - ☐ we'll talk about them over the phone
   - ☐ we won't bother to communicate every day, but we'll try to catch some time if necessary
   - ☐ we won't talk about them

7. How much privacy do you intend to allow one another (i.e. are there some things that you won't communicate)?
    - □ I want to maintain my privacy; I'll let my husband know what's happening when I think it's necessary to do so
    - □ I want to maintain my privacy, so if something happens to me (e.g. at work) and it doesn't affect my husband, I won't talk about it
    - □ I don't want my husband to feel extra stress about my problems (e.g. work problems, health problems, money problems), so I won't tell him about them
    - □ I won't tell my husband anything that might hurt his feelings
    - □ I won't repeat gossip
    - □ I expect to be able to keep a friend or family member's secrets or confidences
    - □ I don't want privacy; I want to tell my husband everything and I expect him to do the same with me

8. How comfortable are you talking about your feelings with your fiancé?
    - □ very comfortable
    - □ fairly comfortable
    - □ not really comfortable
    - □ I hate all that sappy stuff

9. How comfortable are you about confronting your fiancé with something that's upsetting you?
    - □ very comfortable
    - □ fairly comfortable as long as I catch him in a good mood
    - □ it depends on the topic
    - □ not really comfortable (I'm afraid he'll reject me or laugh at me)
    - □ terrified (I hate confrontation)

Chapter 5

Anger

Case Study

Three police cars rolled through the gated golf-course community, sirens blaring. Six officers emerged with their hands on their guns and surrounded the expensive executive home. After a while, neighbors saw the wife led away in handcuffs. Word was that she had threatened her husband with a knife—and not for the first time. "I can't believe I didn't know about her temper before I married her," her husband confided to a friend.

QUIZ

1. How do you express anger?
   - ☐ I get violent (e.g. I hit someone)
   - ☐ I get physical (e.g. I throw things, slam doors)
   - ☐ I verbally threaten someone
   - ☐ I storm away and refuse to talk
   - ☐ I shout
   - ☐ I raise my voice slightly
   - ☐ I refuse to look at the person with whom I'm angry (I freeze the person out)
   - ☐ I refuse to speak to the person with whom I'm angry
   - ☐ I talk negatively about the person behind his/her back
   - ☐ I go for a walk to think and to cool off
   - ☐ I cry
   - ☐ I try to resolve my anger by talking to someone I trust
   - ☐ I sigh, but I don't say anything
   - ☐ I repress or ignore it
   - ☐ I try to resolve the conflict constructively by discussing it with the person with whom I'm angry and listening to his/her point of view
   - ☐ I might write a letter that carefully expressed my feelings and send it to the person who made me angry
   - ☐ other ______________________________

2. If you are angry about something, do you become generally angry or irritable with everyone, even if they're not involved?
   - ☐ yes
   - ☐ no
   - ☐ sometimes
   - ☐ yes, but I warn my family that I'm in a bad mood

3. How do you calm yourself down when you're angry?
   - ☐ I need to physically harm the person with whom I'm angry
   - ☐ I pick a physical fight with anyone I can find
   - ☐ I need to release my anger physically (e.g. I go to the gym for a work out)
   - ☐ I start an argument with anyone I can find
   - ☐ I vent verbally to no one in particular
   - ☐ I cry
   - ☐ I need to express everything I feel to the person with whom I'm angry
   - ☐ I require an apology
   - ☐ I take a deep breath and count to ten
   - ☐ I bottle it up
   - ☐ other ______________________________

4. How long do you tend to stay angry?
   - ☐ forever (I hold a grudge)
   - ☐ a long time (e.g. years)
   - ☐ for a day or two
   - ☐ for the rest of the day
   - ☐ not for long—maybe an hour
   - ☐ until it's resolved

Reading Tip

Make sure you and your fiancé agree about whether this quiz will be confidential and to what extent. For more reading tips, see the Introduction.

5. If your husband did something that made you angry, how would you approach him?
   - ☐ I'd calmly tell him how I feel and negotiate a peace that we can both live with
   - ☐ I'd try to think of some way I can start to make peace, perhaps by acknowledging some fault of mine
   - ☐ I'd ignore him until he realizes I am angry and asks me why; then I'd tell him and we'd try to work it out
   - ☐ I'd expect him to know that I'm angry and why (even if I don't tell him), because he should know me well enough to figure it out
   - ☐ I'd yell at him for other things, without letting him know why I'm really angry
   - ☐ I'd yell at him, letting him know exactly why I'm angry
   - ☐ I'd bring up every fight we ever had and everything he has ever done wrong in the process of letting him know I'm angry

6. If your husband did something to upset you and then apologized, how would you feel?
   - ☐ I'd forgive him and feel glad that it was over
   - ☐ I'd forgive him, but I'd have trouble forgetting it
   - ☐ I'd forgive him, but I would probably bring it up again in a later argument
   - ☐ I'd have trouble forgiving him right away
   - ☐ I'd forgive him once I felt he'd suffered enough
   - ☐ I would not forgive him

7. Assuming that the argument is significant (i.e. not just one that was the result of one of you being grumpy), what would you do if your husband wasn't sorry and you could not resolve your argument?
   - ☐ I'd insist that we go for marriage counseling
   - ☐ I'd repress my feelings
   - ☐ I'd forgive him (whether or not he asked for forgiveness) and move on
   - ☐ I'd be miserable and cranky
   - ☐ I'd nag him about it
   - ☐ I'd file for divorce
   - ☐ other ______________________________

8. If you found out you were in the wrong in an argument, what would you do?
   - ☐ I'd apologize and try not to do it again
   - ☐ I'd give my husband a gift (e.g. chocolates), but I wouldn't apologize
   - ☐ I'd pretend the argument didn't happen
   - ☐ I'd continue to deny that I did anything wrong and blame my husband
   - ☐ I'd initiate sex
   - ☐ other ______________________________

9. Do you believe in going to bed angry with your husband?
   - ☐ yes
   - ☐ no
   - ☐ if it can't be helped

10. If you were angry, would you ever leave your husband to go stay elsewhere for the night?
    - ☐ yes
    - ☐ maybe
    - ☐ probably not
    - ☐ no

11. Would you ever ask your husband to leave (e.g. throw him out)?
    - ☐ yes
    - ☐ maybe
    - ☐ probably not
    - ☐ no

12. If your fiancé is angry, but not at you, how does he treat you?
    - ☐ he hits me
    - ☐ he threatens to harm me
    - ☐ he yells at me
    - ☐ he's irritable with everyone, including me
    - ☐ he avoids me (so as not to take his anger out on me)
    - ☐ he gives me fair warning that he is feeling angry
    - ☐ he does not treat me any differently

13. If your fiancé is irritable or angry about something unrelated to you, how do you respond to his mood?
    - ☐ I try to ignore it
    - ☐ I tiptoe around him, trying to make sure he doesn't focus his anger on me
    - ☐ I tell him I sympathize (i.e. I support him and listen to him)
    - ☐ I sympathize, at least until he lashes out at me
    - ☐ I tell him he's grumpy and ask him not to take it out on me
    - ☐ I get angry back and probably argue

14. If your fiancé is angry with you, how does he express it?
    - ☐ he gets violent
    - ☐ he gets physical (e.g. he throws things)
    - ☐ he verbally threatens me
    - ☐ he slams doors
    - ☐ he storms away and refuses to talk
    - ☐ he shouts
    - ☐ he raises his voice slightly
    - ☐ he brings up every fight we ever had and everything I have ever done wrong in the process of letting me know he's angry
    - ☐ he refuses to look at me (he freezes me out)
    - ☐ he refuses to speak to me
    - ☐ he talks negatively about me behind my back
    - ☐ he goes for a walk to think and to cool off
    - ☐ he cries
    - ☐ he tries to resolve his anger by talking to someone he trusts
    - ☐ he sighs, but doesn't say anything
    - ☐ he represses or ignores it
    - ☐ he tries to resolve the conflict constructively by discussing it with me and listening to my point of view
    - ☐ he might write a letter that carefully expresses his feelings and give it to me
    - ☐ other ____________________

15. Is there a line you can agree not to cross when you're angry with one another?
    - ☐ no violence (e.g. pushing, hitting)
    - ☐ no damaging property
    - ☐ no threatening physical harm
    - ☐ no verbal abuse (calling each other names)
    - ☐ no shouting

16. If you have children, will you argue in front of them?
    - ☐ yes, because we can't help it we're so angry
    - ☐ yes, to teach them how to argue fairly and constructively
    - ☐ I don't know
    - ☐ no, we will try not to
    - ☐ no, it is inappropriate to do so

17. If you are angry, do you sometimes say things you regret later?
    - ☐ always
    - ☐ sometimes
    - ☐ rarely
    - ☐ never

18. Would you verbally abuse your husband (e.g. calling him stupid, good-for-nothing, etc.)?
    - ☐ yes
    - ☐ yes, when I'm trying to be funny
    - ☐ not usually
    - ☐ no

19. As an adult, have you ever physically hurt another person when angry?
    - ☐ yes
    - ☐ yes, it's part of my job (e.g. military personnel, police officer)
    - ☐ yes, while playing sports
    - ☐ yes, in self-defense (e.g. if someone were breaking into my house)
    - ☐ yes, but the other person started it
    - ☐ no, never

20. Have you ever used or brandished a weapon in a physical confrontation?
    - ☐ yes
    - ☐ yes, it's part of my job (e.g. military personnel, police officer)
    - ☐ yes, while playing sports (e.g. hockey stick)
    - ☐ no

21. Have you ever intentionally physically hurt or threatened a man?
    - ☐ yes
    - ☐ no

22. How would you respond if your husband called you names (i.e. verbal abuse)?
    - □ I'd laugh it off
    - □ I'd ignore him
    - □ I'd blame myself, thinking I deserved it
    - □ I'd be quiet and take the abuse
    - □ I'd be ashamed and not tell anybody
    - □ I'd get so angry I would respond with physical force
    - □ I'd respond with similar verbal or emotional abuse
    - □ I'd explain that he was hurting my feelings and ask him to stop
    - □ I'd call a friend or relative for support
    - □ I'd leave
    - □ I'd escape the relationship permanently

23. How would you respond to threats of physical abuse from your husband?
    - □ I'd laugh it off
    - □ I'd ignore him
    - □ I'd be frightened
    - □ I'd tell him to back off
    - □ I'd be intimidated, but I wouldn't let on
    - □ I'd feel responsible (i.e. thinking I deserved it)
    - □ I'd be quiet and take it
    - □ I'd be ashamed and not tell anybody
    - □ I'd threaten physical abuse back
    - □ I'd hurt him first
    - □ I'd call a friend or relative for support
    - □ I'd leave
    - □ I'd escape the relationship permanently
    - □ I'd call the police

24. How would you respond to physical abuse?
    - □ I'd laugh it off
    - □ I'd be frightened
    - □ I'd tell him to back off
    - □ I'd feel responsible (i.e. thinking I deserved it)
    - □ I'd be quiet and take the abuse
    - □ I'd be ashamed and not tell anybody
    - □ I'd threaten physical force back
    - □ I'd fight back
    - □ I'd call a friend or relative for support
    - □ I'd leave
    - □ I'd escape the relationship permanently
    - □ I'd call the police

Chapter 6

Children

Case Study

Gilda and Aaron married late in life. Both were in their early forties when the two college professors met at an Amnesty International conference and fell in love. They shared many common interests and were politically active. Although they had never discussed children, Gilda felt her biological clock ticking. She approached Aaron about having a baby, knowing this would be a surprise to him. "I decided years ago that I didn't want to bring a child into this troubled, overcrowded world," he told her. "That's why I had a vasectomy when I was thirty." Gilda couldn't reconcile herself to remaining childless. Six months later, she divorced Aaron, re-married and became a mother after a program of fertility treatments.

QUIZ

1. Do you want children?
   - ☐ yes
   - ☐ no
   - ☐ I'm not sure

2. How many children do you want?
   - ☐ 1
   - ☐ 2
   - ☐ 3
   - ☐ 4
   - ☐ 5
   - ☐ 6
   - ☐ 6+
   - ☐ it depends on how easy or difficult pregnancy and birth are for me (and my husband)
   - ☐ I don't approve of birth control (or I won't use it), so however many we have is fine with me

3. Why do you want children?
   - ☐ so part of my husband and I will live on
   - ☐ because everyone has them
   - ☐ because my family is pressuring me
   - ☐ so I can live vicariously through my children
   - ☐ to provide us with a fuller, more meaningful life

4. When do you want children?
   - ☐ any time after I'm married
   - ☐ after I'm married, but have had some time to adjust to the marriage
   - ☐ any time after I'm 30
   - ☐ not until I'm successful in my career
   - ☐ not until we can financially afford to
   - ☐ as soon as possible
   - ☐ before I'm 40

Reading Tip

Answer based on how you feel now, not how you think you'll feel in the future. For more reading tips, see the Introduction.

5. How important is it to you to have a particular sex (boy or girl)?
   - ☐ very
   - ☐ somewhat
   - ☐ it doesn't matter

6. If it is important, which sex do you absolutely want?
   - ☐ boy
   - ☐ girl

7. If you want a particular sex and don't get it right away, how many children would you have to try to get the other sex?
   - ☐ 1
   - ☐ 2
   - ☐ 3
   - ☐ 4
   - ☐ 5
   - ☐ 6
   - ☐ 6+

8. What would you do if you found yourself expecting a baby at a time when you didn't want one?
   - ☐ I'd treat the baby as I would one that I planned
   - ☐ I'd have the baby, but continue with my other priorities, leaving the baby to others (e.g. grandparents)
   - ☐ I'd have the baby, and then put the child up for adoption
   - ☐ I'd have an abortion

9. What would you do if you found out <u>you</u> are physically unable to have a child?
   - ☐ we'd adopt through standard channels
   - ☐ we'd adopt privately by supporting a needy unwed mother
   - ☐ we'd adopt internationally
   - ☐ we'd consider a surrogate mother
   - ☐ we'd adjust and go on with life as it was
   - ☐ we'd try mild medical interventions
   - ☐ we'd try aggressive medical interventions

10. What would you do if you found out your husband was unable to father a child?
    - ☐ we'd adopt through standard channels
    - ☐ we'd adopt privately by supporting a needy unwed mother
    - ☐ we'd adopt internationally
    - ☐ we'd consider a sperm donor
    - ☐ we'd adjust and go on with life as it was
    - ☐ we'd try mild medical interventions
    - ☐ we'd try aggressive medical interventions
    - ☐ I'd divorce him and try in my next marriage

11. In order of priorities, how would you rank the following (1 being the most important)?

	Rank
☐ career/work	____
☐ spouse	____
☐ children	____
☐ extended family	____
☐ friends	____
☐ clubs	____
☐ church	____
☐ hobbies	____
☐ sports	____
☐ other ______________________________	____

12. Will one parent stay home with the children?
    - ☐ yes
    - ☐ yes, until they go to school
    - ☐ ideally, yes
    - ☐ we'd work shift work so one parent is with the children most of the time
    - ☐ no
    - ☐ I don't know

13. If yes, which of you will stay home with the children?
    - □ I will
    - □ my husband will
    - □ we both will (e.g. shift work)
    - □ it doesn't matter

14. Who do you think should be the one to make judgment calls about how to handle the children?
    - □ I will
    - □ my husband will
    - □ we both will, arriving at decisions co-operatively
    - □ whoever feels more strongly about the issue will
    - □ an independent adviser will (e.g. guidance counselor, grandparent, babysitter)
    - □ I don't know

15. If the child is sick, which of you will take care of the child (e.g. get up in the night, take off work)?
    - □ I will
    - □ my husband will
    - □ we both will
    - □ we'll take turns
    - □ I don't know

16. When your child is sick, who will decide when he/she needs medical attention?
    - □ my husband and I together will decide
    - □ my husband will decide
    - □ I will decide
    - □ the child will decide (assuming he/she is old enough to say)
    - □ whoever is willing to go to the doctor or to the hospital with him/her will decide
    - □ other ______________________________

17. How would you feel about having your child sleep with you and your husband?
    - □ no way; I want my privacy and my husband belongs with me
    - □ children need to be taught that there are some things that they can't join in and our sleeping arrangement is one of those things
    - □ it would be okay if it were only for a little while (e.g. if the child is sick or has a nightmare)
    - □ I would agree to it only when the child is small (e.g. 4 years old or younger)
    - □ I'd be okay with it if the child slept in our room, but not in our bed
    - □ I'd enjoy having our child sleep with us
    - □ I don't know how I'd feel

18. How much time would you expect to spend in the company of your children?
    - ☐ less than 1/2 hour a day (e.g. if I'm away on business a lot)
    - ☐ 1/2 hour a day
    - ☐ 1 hour a day
    - ☐ 1 to 3 hours a day
    - ☐ 3 to 5 hours a day
    - ☐ 5 to 10 hours a day (e.g. if I worked part-time)
    - ☐ 5 to 24 hours a day (e.g. if I was a stay-at-home parent)

19. How much time would you expect your husband to spend in the company of your children?
    - ☐ less than 1/2 hour a day (e.g. if he's away a lot on business)
    - ☐ 1/2 hour a day
    - ☐ 1 hour a day
    - ☐ 1 to 3 hours a day
    - ☐ 3 to 5 hours a day
    - ☐ 5 tot 10 hours a day (e.g. if he worked part-time)
    - ☐ 5 to 24 hours a day (e.g. if he was a stay-at-home parent)

20. How often would you like to go out alone with your husband after you have children?
    - ☐ once a week
    - ☐ once a month
    - ☐ once every few months (at least when they're little)
    - ☐ frequent weekends away together (e.g. every month or two)

21. What interests would you try to maintain after having children?
    - ☐ clubs (e.g. Bridge club)
    - ☐ sporting activity (watching or playing)
    - ☐ church
    - ☐ private times with friends
    - ☐ going to bars/pubs
    - ☐ other ____________________

22. How many interests, other than your work, would you try to maintain over and above family life (e.g. a sport, club or friends)?
    - ☐ none
    - ☐ 1 night or day a month
    - ☐ 1 night or day a week
    - ☐ 2 nights or days a week
    - ☐ 3 nights or days a week
    - ☐ 4 nights or days a week
    - ☐ 5 nights or days a week
    - ☐ 6 nights or days a week
    - ☐ 7 nights or days a week

23. Would your interests involve your husband?
    - ☐ yes
    - ☐ no
    - ☐ sometimes

24. How many interests do you think your husband should maintain over and above family life?
    - ☐ none
    - ☐ 1 night or day a month
    - ☐ 1 night or day a week
    - ☐ 2 nights or days a week
    - ☐ 3 nights or days a week
    - ☐ 4 nights or days a week
    - ☐ 5 nights or days a week
    - ☐ 6 nights or days a week
    - ☐ 7 nights or days a week

25. If both of you continue to work, you will need a babysitter. What type of babysitter would you want?
    - ☐ a family member (e.g. grandparent)
    - ☐ a day care
    - ☐ private babysitting
    - ☐ a nanny
    - ☐ a full-time parent accomplished by juggling schedules with my husband

26. What sort of location do you want to be in when raising your children?
    - ☐ a large city
    - ☐ a small city
    - ☐ a town
    - ☐ a village
    - ☐ the country (e.g. farm or ranch)
    - ☐ a foreign country

27. In what sort of housing do you want to raise children?
    - ☐ a condo or apartment in the city
    - ☐ a townhouse
    - ☐ a house
    - ☐ a house in the suburbs
    - ☐ a farm or ranch
    - ☐ a trailer park
    - ☐ other ____________________

28. What is your philosophy of parenting?
   - ☐ children should be free to do whatever they want; they should not be hindered in any way in their exploration
   - ☐ children need a great deal of peer interaction and freedom to be with their friends; friendship is one of the most important aspects of childhood
   - ☐ children under 8 years of age should be closely supervised at all times by an adult
   - ☐ children can be supervised by older siblings
   - ☐ children should be carefully guided and corrected
   - ☐ children should be respected as individuals, but given boundaries of appropriate behavior
   - ☐ children should be seen and not heard; adults come first, children second
   - ☐ children should be given a strong authority figure and instructed to obey this authority without question
   - ☐ other ________________________________

29. It is a fact that how we are treated as children affects who we become as adults. Given this, how were you disciplined as a child?
   - ☐ I was abused (e.g. beaten)
   - ☐ I was spanked
   - ☐ I was given gentle slaps on my hand or bottom
   - ☐ I was given time outs
   - ☐ I was verbally reprimanded
   - ☐ I was given a calm explanation of why my behavior was bad
   - ☐ I was yelled at
   - ☐ my privileges were revoked (e.g. I was not allowed to watch TV)
   - ☐ I was sent to my room
   - ☐ I was grounded
   - ☐ I was never disciplined
   - ☐ I don't remember

30. What do you feel is appropriate discipline for children?
   - ☐ spanking
   - ☐ gentle slaps on the hand or bottom
   - ☐ time outs
   - ☐ verbal reprimands
   - ☐ a calm explanation of why the behavior was bad
   - ☐ yelling
   - ☐ revoking their privileges
   - ☐ sending them to their rooms
   - ☐ grounding them
   - ☐ none
   - ☐ it depends on the child
   - ☐ other ________________________________

31. Your future husband needs to know—were you abused as a child?
    - ☐ yes
    - ☐ no

32. If yes, how?
    - ☐ I was locked or tied up
    - ☐ I was sexually abused
    - ☐ I was physically abused (e.g. beaten)
    - ☐ I was denied food
    - ☐ I was verbally abused (e.g. told I was stupid, no good, etc.)
    - ☐ other ______________________________

33. Do you wish to live near your parents (your child's grandparents)?
    - ☐ yes
    - ☐ yes, but not in the same neighborhood
    - ☐ yes, within driving distance, but not in the same city
    - ☐ no

34. Do you wish to live near your husband's parents (your child's grandparents)?
    - ☐ yes
    - ☐ yes, but not in the same neighborhood
    - ☐ yes, within driving distance, but not in the same city
    - ☐ no

35. How much discretion would you permit your parents in raising your child?
    - ☐ they'd have the same authority as my husband and I have
    - ☐ they'd be the full-time babysitter, but they would work within the rules that we set out (e.g. no spanking, specific food choices)
    - ☐ they'd be our favorite babysitter, but they would have no authority to punish
    - ☐ they would only see the child when I or my husband is present
    - ☐ they would not be involved with our child

36. How much discretion would you permit your husband's parents in raising your child?
    - ☐ they'd have the same authority as my husband and I have
    - ☐ they'd be the full-time babysitter, but they would work within the rules that we set out (e.g. no spanking, specific food choices)
    - ☐ they'd be our favorite babysitter, but they would have no authority to punish
    - ☐ they would only see the child when I or my husband is present
    - ☐ they would not be involved with our child

37. What would you do if you felt that leaving your child with a particular family member was putting that child at risk (perhaps of injuring himself/herself, or being abused in some way)?
    - ☐ I would not allow our child to visit or see that family member
    - ☐ I would insist that my husband or I be present whenever that family member is with our child
    - ☐ I would let our child go, but I'd hope for the best (after all, the person is family)
    - ☐ I never suffered as a child, even when with neglectful care givers, so our child would be okay

38. What would you do if you and your husband disagreed about whether a particular family member poses a threat (i.e. harm or danger) to your child?
    - ☐ if the person was a member of my family, I'd expect my husband to accept my assessment (after all, I know my family better than he does)
    - ☐ if the person was a member of my husband's family, I'd go along with his assessment
    - ☐ we'd talk it out and try to reach a meeting of the minds, or at least a compromise
    - ☐ we'd play it safe, just in case (at the very least, making sure one of us is there with the child)

Chapter 7

Money

Case Study

Juanita and Reg had struggled financially for a number of years, and now had a little extra money each month. Juanita wanted to save for their retirement, but Reg wanted to save for a dream vacation. "My parents saved all their lives for their retirements, but then my Dad died before they could do anything they had planned," he said. "I want to enjoy life now, while we're young and healthy."

QUIZ

1. Do you both intend to have jobs and earn money?
   - ☐ yes
   - ☐ no, only one of us will work
   - ☐ no
   - ☐ I'm not sure

2. Once you're married, do you plan to pool your money together into one household fund used by both of you?
   - ☐ yes
   - ☐ no

3. If yes, who will decide about expenditures?
   - ☐ I will
   - ☐ my husband will
   - ☐ we'll decide together
   - ☐ we'll divide the responsibility (e.g. one of us will make decisions about transportation, the other about food)

4. If you don't plan to pool your money together, how will the money be handled?
   - ☐ we'll keep separate bank accounts and divide up expenses like roommates
   - ☐ my husband will pay for all living expenses leaving my income to be spent at my discretion
   - ☐ I will pay for all living expenses leaving my husband's income to be spent at his discretion

5. Who do you think will be the primary breadwinner?
   - ☐ I will be
   - ☐ my husband will be
   - ☐ it may change back and forth over time

Reading Tip

If your answer is not listed, write it in the margin. For more reading tips, see the Introduction.

6. Do you believe in buying on credit?
   - ☐ yes
   - ☐ yes, for large items (e.g. furniture)
   - ☐ yes, in moderation (e.g. bills not to exceed $500)
   - ☐ no

7. Do you think it is okay to carry over a monthly balance on credit cards?
   - ☐ yes
   - ☐ no
   - ☐ not normally, but under special circumstances it's okay

8. Who is going to take responsibility for seeing that the bills get paid?
   - ☐ I will
   - ☐ my husband will
   - ☐ we both will by dividing them up
   - ☐ we both will by doing them together

9. Is there a time when you would expect to have less than two incomes?
   - ☐ yes
   - ☐ no

10. If yes, when would that be?
    - ☐ when we have children
    - ☐ when my parents get old and require constant care
    - ☐ when my husband's parents get old and require constant care
    - ☐ if either my husband or I should get sick or injured
    - ☐ if either my husband or I become temporarily unemployed
    - ☐ other ______________________________

11. If only one partner is working, does that give him/her more power to determine spending?
    - ☐ yes
    - ☐ yes, within reason
    - ☐ no (the other person's contributions, although not monetary, are worthy of value)

12. Have you ever kept a budget?
    - ☐ yes
    - ☐ no
    - ☐ only for work

13. Do you plan to live on a budget when you are married?
    - ☐ yes
    - ☐ no
    - ☐ I don't know

14. Do you expect your husband to live on a pre-determined budget?
    - ☐ yes
    - ☐ no

15. Who will set the budget?
    - ☐ I will
    - ☐ my husband will
    - ☐ whoever is better at math or with money will do it
    - ☐ we will set it together
    - ☐ an outside adviser will set the budget (e.g. bank, financial adviser, parents)
    - ☐ we will not have a budget

16. What do you like to spend your money on?
    - ☐ house (e.g. saving for a house or paying off the mortgage)
    - ☐ cottage
    - ☐ cars
    - ☐ boat
    - ☐ high-tech toys
    - ☐ dinners out
    - ☐ entertainment
    - ☐ vacations
    - ☐ jewelry
    - ☐ clothes
    - ☐ house improvements (e.g. re-decorating)
    - ☐ early retirement savings
    - ☐ children's education fund
    - ☐ charity, church or equivalent
    - ☐ loans to friends or family
    - ☐ other ____________________

17. In order of priorities, rank what you think are the most important monetary expenditures to the least important (1 being the most important).

	Rank
☐ house	____
☐ cottage	____
☐ cars	____
☐ boat	____
☐ high-tech toys	____
☐ dinners out	____
☐ entertainment	____
☐ vacations	____
☐ jewelry	____
☐ clothes	____
☐ house improvements (e.g. re-decorating)	____
☐ early retirement savings	____
☐ children's education fund	____
☐ charity, church or equivalent	____
☐ loans to friends or family	____
☐ other ______________________________	____

18. Do you expect these priorities to change once you are married?
    - ☐ yes
    - ☐ no

19. Would your husband need to consult you before buying something?
    - ☐ yes
    - ☐ no
    - ☐ it depends how much it is

20. Will you agree to a certain amount of money that can be discretionary (i.e. your husband does not have to consult you about a purchase under this amount of money)?
    - ☐ yes
    - ☐ yes, he will have an allowance to spend, but he cannot exceed it
    - ☐ yes, we'll each have an allowance to spend as we see fit
    - ☐ no, we can spend as much as we want without consulting each other

21. If yes, what will be that amount?
    - ☐ it will be determined by our budget
    - ☐ $25.00
    - ☐ $50.00
    - ☐ $75.00
    - ☐ $100.00
    - ☐ $200.00
    - ☐ $500.00
    - ☐ over $500.00

22. Is that set amount of money the same for both partners?
    - ☐ yes
    - ☐ no

23. Who will decide on the type of investments you undertake?
    - ☐ I will
    - ☐ my husband will
    - ☐ whoever is better at math or with money will decide
    - ☐ we will decide together
    - ☐ an outside adviser will handle our investments (e.g. bank, financial adviser, parents)

24. When do you plan to start saving for your child's education?
    - ☐ never, we don't plan to have children
    - ☐ never, the child can pay his/her own way through school
    - ☐ never, a high-school education is good enough
    - ☐ now
    - ☐ as soon as the child is born
    - ☐ when the child becomes a teenager
    - ☐ the year before our child plans to attend college

25. When do you plan to start saving for your retirement?
    - ☐ right away
    - ☐ 10 years from now
    - ☐ 20 years from now
    - ☐ never

26. Do you plan to acquire life insurance once you are married?
    - ☐ yes
    - ☐ no
    - ☐ I don't know
    - ☐ yes, after we have children
    - ☐ yes, later

27. If yes, how much coverage will you get?
    - ☐ enough to pay off our house
    - ☐ 3 or more years worth of my annual income (e.g. if my annual income is $30,000, I'd take out $90,000 worth of life insurance)
    - ☐ 1 or 2 years of my annual income
    - ☐ enough to pay for funeral arrangements
    - ☐ as much as we can afford
    - ☐ other ____

Chapter 8

Careers

Case Study

Wayne and Janice both worked in the insurance industry. One day, after completing a two-year management course at night school, Janice was offered a major promotion. Not only would it mean a cross-country move, but Janice would be earning quite a lot more than Wayne. Wayne was not sure he wanted to move, and was even less sure about not being the primary breadwinner in the family.

QUIZ

1. Do you have a job?
   - ☐ yes
   - ☐ no

2. How do you view your job?
   - ☐ a burden
   - ☐ a way to make money
   - ☐ a way to support a family
   - ☐ a career
   - ☐ a way to move up in the world
   - ☐ a way to fulfil my dreams
   - ☐ a pleasure (I get personal satisfaction from a job well done)
   - ☐ a way to help people (e.g. as a doctor)
   - ☐ other ____________________

3. Is the job you are in the one that you always hoped for?
   - ☐ yes
   - ☐ no

4. If no, do you think you will need further education to get the job you want?
   - ☐ yes
   - ☐ no
   - ☐ maybe

5. What sacrifices, if any, would you expect of your husband while you pursue further education?
   - ☐ my husband would have to earn enough money to cover all our living expenses and put me through school
   - ☐ I would work part-time, but my husband would pay for most of our living expenses
   - ☐ we would put off certain goals (e.g. buying a house, having children) until I have completed my education
   - ☐ my husband would not have as much time with me
   - ☐ my husband would have to care for any children we might have
   - ☐ my husband would not be affected in any way
   - ☐ I don't intend to pursue further education of any sort

6. If you are furthering your education, do you think that your husband should also further his education so that you remain intellectually compatible?
   - ☐ yes
   - ☐ no

7. What sacrifices would you be willing to make if your husband chose to further his education?
   - ☐ I would be happy to financially support our household and put my husband through school
   - ☐ I would be willing to work part-time
   - ☐ I would be willing to see less of my husband as long as it was only for a pre-determined period of time
   - ☐ I would be willing to put off certain goals (e.g. buying a house, having children) until he has completed his education
   - ☐ I would be willing to care for any children we might have
   - ☐ I would not be willing to make any sacrifices; I am not in favor of him pursuing further education

8. Who do you think should earn more money in a marriage?
   - ☐ the husband
   - ☐ the wife
   - ☐ it doesn't matter

Reading Tip

After you've finished a chapter (or the whole book), compare your answers with your fiancé's. For more reading tips, see the Introduction.

9. If something should happen where your husband's career really takes off and he earns a lot more money than you, how would you feel?
   - ☐ happy that my husband is successful
   - ☐ relieved that I'm not primarily responsible for earning money for our household
   - ☐ relieved that I won't have to work so hard
   - ☐ resentful
   - ☐ inadequate
   - ☐ angry
   - ☐ I wouldn't be able to handle it

10. If you felt negatively about your husband's career, how would you handle those feelings?
    - ☐ I'd say nothing, burying them for as long as possible
    - ☐ I'd talk to my husband about them
    - ☐ I'd seek counseling
    - ☐ I'd re-direct my own career to something fulfilling
    - ☐ I'd focus on home life (e.g. children)
    - ☐ I might have an affair
    - ☐ I might seek a divorce
    - ☐ other ______________________________

11. If you receive a promotion, which entails moving, would you consult your husband before accepting?
    - ☐ yes
    - ☐ no
    - ☐ I don't know

12. If you get transferred or receive a promotion, should your husband be willing to move, even if it means giving up his job?
    - ☐ no
    - ☐ yes, as long as he gets transferred, too
    - ☐ yes, as long as there are career opportunities for him in the new location
    - ☐ yes, as long as we are moving to somewhere within a 200-mile radius
    - ☐ yes, as long as we are moving within the same country
    - ☐ yes, no matter where it is

13. If your husband gets transferred or receives a promotion which entails moving, would you be willing to do so, even if it means giving up your own job?
    - ☐ no
    - ☐ yes, as long as I get transferred, too
    - ☐ yes, as long as there are career opportunities for me in the new location
    - ☐ yes, as long as we are moving to somewhere within a 200-mile radius
    - ☐ yes, as long as we are moving within the same country
    - ☐ yes, no matter where it is

14. Does your current job entail travel away from home (e.g. overnight)?
    - ☐ no
    - ☐ yes, some (1 to 3 weeks per year total)
    - ☐ yes, a lot (3 to 6 weeks per year total)
    - ☐ yes, constantly (e.g. travelling sales representative, pilot, truck driver)
    - ☐ yes, for long periods (e.g. a professional working under contract for a specified period of time)

15. If no, would you be willing, if it came up, to accept a job that requires a lot of travelling?
    - ☐ yes
    - ☐ no
    - ☐ I don't know

16. Do you think your husband will need to travel with his job?
    - ☐ no
    - ☐ yes, some (1 to 3 weeks per year total)
    - ☐ yes, a lot (3 to 6 weeks per year total)
    - ☐ yes, constantly (e.g. travelling sales representative, pilot, truck driver)
    - ☐ yes, for long periods (e.g. a professional working under contract for a specified period of time)

17. Would you want your husband to keep a job that entails a lot of travel?
    - ☐ yes, I know what he does for a living
    - ☐ yes, if he wants to
    - ☐ it would be okay, but not ideal
    - ☐ no, I don't want him away a lot

18. If you are travelling, what would you expect of your husband?
    - ☐ he should call me every day on my cell phone or at my hotel
    - ☐ he should call me every few days
    - ☐ he doesn't need to call
    - ☐ he should come with me
    - ☐ he should stay at home and hold down the fort
    - ☐ he should take the opportunity to spend time with some of his family or friends that I don't care for

19. If your husband is travelling, what do you expect from him?
    - ☐ he should call home every day
    - ☐ he should call home every few days
    - ☐ he doesn't need to call
    - ☐ I'd like to be invited to go along
    - ☐ I'd like him to bring home some gifts or souvenirs
    - ☐ other ____________________

20. If you work shift work and work at conflicting schedules to your husband's schedule, how would you keep the relationship working?
    - ☐ we'd try to arrange time off together at least once a week
    - ☐ we'd leave notes for each other
    - ☐ we'd phone frequently
    - ☐ we'd wait until vacation time for quality time together
    - ☐ we won't worry about it

21. Is your job ever life threatening (e.g. fire fighter, police officer)?
    - ☐ yes
    - ☐ sometimes
    - ☐ rarely
    - ☐ no

22. If yes, will the life-threatening aspects of your job ever spill over into your family life (e.g. a police detective might receive death threats that encompass his/her family)?
    - ☐ yes
    - ☐ possibly
    - ☐ no

23. If your fiancé is involved in a dangerous line of work, how do you think you'll handle the emotional stress once you're married?
    - ☐ I'll pretend he is in no danger (e.g. like an ostrich)
    - ☐ I'll pray a lot
    - ☐ I'll have a difficult time adjusting
    - ☐ other ________________________________

Chapter 9

Family and In-Laws

Case Study

Ivan knew that Josephine's mother, Thelma, didn't like him. After all, he had stolen away her daughter. Nevertheless, when Thelma could no longer manage her rambling country house, Ivan reluctantly agreed that she could live with them. Six months later, he had had enough. "She monopolizes your time with her pointless gossip, she tells the kids they don't have to obey our rules, and she's always criticizing and insulting me in front of everyone," he pointedly explained to Josephine. "I can't stand it any more. Either she goes or I do!"

QUIZ

1. What type of family were you part of as a child?
   - ☐ two parents and siblings
   - ☐ two parents with me as an only child
   - ☐ one parent and siblings
   - ☐ one parent with me as an only child
   - ☐ one parent, siblings and parent's live-in boyfriend or girlfriend
   - ☐ one parent and parent's live-in boyfriend or girlfriend
   - ☐ one parent and a long line of live-in boyfriends or girlfriends (with or without siblings)
   - ☐ a dysfunctional family
   - ☐ an abusive home environment
   - ☐ foster care
   - ☐ I was a street kid
   - ☐ relatives (e.g. grandparents) raised me
   - ☐ other ______________________________

2. Was your childhood family life...
   - ☐ mostly happy
   - ☐ mostly unhappy
   - ☐ sometimes happy, sometimes unhappy (at different points in life)

3. What is your current relationship with your mother?
   - ☐ my mother and I get along great
   - ☐ I still live with my mother
   - ☐ I live right near her and see her often
   - ☐ I talk with my mother on the phone regularly
   - ☐ in times of crisis, my mother can be counted on to help
   - ☐ I am on speaking terms with my mother, but not much more
   - ☐ I rarely see or hear from my mother
   - ☐ I ignore my mother, even when we're together
   - ☐ I have major issues with my mother (e.g. anger)
   - ☐ I want nothing to do with my mother
   - ☐ my mother provides me with little support
   - ☐ my mother abandoned me when I was a child
   - ☐ my mother is no longer living

Reading Tip

After you've completed the quiz, highlight those issues where you and your fiancé gave very different answers. For more reading tips, see the Introduction.

4. What is your current relationship with your father?
   - ☐ my father and I get along great
   - ☐ I still live with my father
   - ☐ I live right near him and see him often
   - ☐ I talk with my father on the phone regularly
   - ☐ in times of crisis, my father can be counted on to help
   - ☐ I am on speaking terms with my father, but not much more
   - ☐ I rarely see or hear from my father
   - ☐ I ignore my father, even when we're together
   - ☐ I have major issues with my father (e.g. anger)
   - ☐ I want nothing to do with my father
   - ☐ my father provides me with little support
   - ☐ my father abandoned me when I was a child
   - ☐ my father is no longer living

5. What is your current relationship with your siblings, if you have any?
   - ☐ I live right near my siblings and see them often
   - ☐ I am on good terms with every member of my family
   - ☐ I am on speaking terms with every member of my family
   - ☐ I rarely see my siblings
   - ☐ I ignore my siblings, even when we're together
   - ☐ I am actively hostile towards one or more of my siblings
   - ☐ I refuse to see one or more of my siblings

6. Once you are married, what will your relationship with your husband's parents be like, based on your current relationship with them?
   - ☐ I have not yet met my in-laws
   - ☐ I'll think my in-laws are marvelous
   - ☐ I'll see them often
   - ☐ I'll be on good terms with my mother-in-law
   - ☐ I'll be on good terms with my father-in-law
   - ☐ I'll rarely see or hear from my husband's parents
   - ☐ I'll be courteous with my in-laws (no matter how I feel) for my husband's sake
   - ☐ I'll ignore my in-laws, even when we're together
   - ☐ I'll strongly dislike my husband's mother
   - ☐ I'll strongly dislike my husband's father
   - ☐ I will not want to have anything to do with them
   - ☐ my husband has major issues with his parents so I will stay out of it
   - ☐ I'll try to keep the peace between my husband and his parents
   - ☐ I'll support my husband's decisions with respect to his parents
   - ☐ my husband's parents have passed away

7. Once you are married, what do you think your relationship with your husband's siblings will be like?
   - ☐ my husband is an only child
   - ☐ I have not yet met my husband's siblings
   - ☐ we'll live right near my husband's siblings and see them often
   - ☐ I'll be on good terms with every member of his family
   - ☐ I'll be on speaking terms with every member of his family
   - ☐ I'll rarely see his siblings
   - ☐ I'll be courteous with them (no matter how I feel) for my husband's sake
   - ☐ I'll ignore his siblings, even when we're together
   - ☐ I'll be actively hostile to one or more member(s) of his family
   - ☐ I will not want to have anything to do with them
   - ☐ I'll like my husband's siblings, even if he doesn't
   - ☐ my husband has major issues with his siblings so I will stay out of it
   - ☐ I'll try to keep the peace between my husband and his siblings
   - ☐ I'll support my husband's decisions with respect to his siblings

8. Would you ever consider moving in with your parents?
   - ☐ yes, if we are financially strapped
   - ☐ yes, but only until we save up enough for a home of our own
   - ☐ yes, to get help with our children
   - ☐ yes, so we can take care of them (my parents)
   - ☐ only if there were no other options
   - ☐ no

9. Would you ever consider moving in with your in-laws?
   - ☐ yes, if we are financially strapped
   - ☐ yes, but only until we save up enough for a home of our own
   - ☐ yes, to get help with our children
   - ☐ yes, so we can take care of them (my husband's parents)
   - ☐ only if there were no other options
   - ☐ no

10. If your family lives far away, how would you feel about family members coming to stay with you for lengthy visits (e.g. a month)?
    - ☐ I'd be happy to see them
    - ☐ I love entertaining, so my home would be their home while they're visiting
    - ☐ I would only be comfortable with the visit if it weren't too long (e.g. a week instead of a month)
    - ☐ I get very tense when I don't have my privacy, so I would not enjoy lengthy visits
    - ☐ I would dread it
    - ☐ I would not want to have anyone stay at our home
    - ☐ I don't know

11. If your husband's family lives far away, how would you feel about his family members coming to stay with you for lengthy visits (e.g. a month)?
    - ☐ I'd be happy to see them
    - ☐ I love entertaining, so my home would be their home while they're visiting
    - ☐ I would only be comfortable with the visit if it weren't too long (e.g. a week instead of a month)
    - ☐ I would be hospitable for my husband's sake
    - ☐ I get very tense when I don't have my privacy, so I would not enjoy lengthy visits
    - ☐ I would dread it
    - ☐ I would not want to have anyone stay at our home
    - ☐ I don't know

12. How much time do you think you will spend with extended family or focused on family-related matters (either yours or your husband's)?
    - ☐ 3 or more hours every day (e.g. we live with one of our parents)
    - ☐ 2 or more hours every day (e.g. taking care of a sick parent)
    - ☐ 1 hour every day
    - ☐ 1/2 hour every day
    - ☐ 3 to 5 hours a week (e.g. Sunday brunch)
    - ☐ 1 hour twice a week (e.g. phoning parents)
    - ☐ 3 to 5 hours a month
    - ☐ a couple of days a year (e.g. home for holidays)
    - ☐ a few weeks a year (e.g. spending vacations together)

13. How much time do you think your husband will spend with extended family or focused on family-related matters (either yours or your husband's)?
    - □ 3 or more hours every day (e.g. we live with one of our parents)
    - □ 2 or more hours per day (e.g. taking care of a sick parent)
    - □ 1 hour every day
    - □ 1/2 hour every day
    - □ 3 to 5 hours a week (e.g. Sunday brunch)
    - □ 1 hour twice a week (e.g. phoning parents)
    - □ 3 to 5 hours a month
    - □ a couple of days a year (e.g. home for holidays)
    - □ a few weeks a year (e.g. spending vacations together)

14. How much influence do you think extended family (i.e. your parents and siblings) should have in your life, compared to your spouse?
    - □ more influence than my husband (after all, my family has known me longer)
    - □ equal influence to my husband
    - □ slightly less influence than my husband
    - □ my husband has greater influence on my life and decisions

15. When making a decision involving you and your husband, how much influence would your parents have regarding the decision?
    - □ they would have a lot of influence (after all, one is supposed to get wiser with age)
    - □ we'd ask them for advice and probably follow it
    - □ we'd listen to their advice, but ultimately make our own decision
    - □ they would badger us until we did what they wanted
    - □ they'd offer unsolicited advice, which we would respectfully listen to, but we'd make our own decision
    - □ they'd offer unsolicited advice and we'd ask them to mind their own business
    - □ they would have no influence at all with respect to the decision

16. When making a decision involving you and your husband, how much influence would your in-laws have regarding the decision?
    - □ they would have a lot of influence (after all, one is supposed to get wiser with age)
    - □ we'd ask them for advice and probably follow it
    - □ we'd listen to their advice, but ultimately make our own decision
    - □ they would badger us until we did what they wanted
    - □ they'd offer unsolicited advice, which we would respectfully listen to, but we'd make our own decision
    - □ they'd offer unsolicited advice and we'd ask them to mind their own business
    - □ they would have no influence at all with respect to the decision

17. How do you plan to structure holidays where both families expect you to be there (e.g. Christmas Day, Thanksgiving)?
    - ☐ we will try to fit in both families on the same day
    - ☐ we will see one family on Christmas Day and the other on Boxing Day
    - ☐ we will alternate years (one year with my family, the next with his)
    - ☐ we will invite both families to participate together at our home
    - ☐ we won't spend the holidays with either family
    - ☐ other ____________________

18. Who will deal with your family with respect to organizing events (e.g. sending Christmas or birthday cards)?
    - ☐ I will
    - ☐ my husband will
    - ☐ we'll both do some of the work
    - ☐ I'll handle my family and he has to handle his
    - ☐ we'll take turns

19. It is common that the wife takes over maintaining family relationships, even within her husband's family (e.g. reminding him to phone, sending his parents cards). Do you plan to do this?
    - ☐ yes
    - ☐ no, my husband should be responsible for his family relationships
    - ☐ no

20. Will you and your husband always attend family events together?
    - ☐ yes, we're a team
    - ☐ yes, if possible
    - ☐ no
    - ☐ it depends

21. If you really couldn't stand your in-laws, but your husband is still in touch with them, how would you handle family events?
    - ☐ I'd insist that both my husband and I <u>not</u> attend the family event
    - ☐ I wouldn't attend, but my husband could do what he wants
    - ☐ I'd try to work out my differences with them
    - ☐ I'd attend the event for my husband's sake (i.e. I'd grin and bear it)

22. If one of either your husband's or your parents got sick (a lengthy illness), what would you do?
    - ☐ we'd provide emotional support
    - ☐ we would move in with him/her temporarily to help out
    - ☐ we'd arrange for him/her to move in with us temporarily
    - ☐ we'd arrange for nursing care in his/her own home
    - ☐ we'd look into Retirement Homes, Old Age homes or Nursing Homes (depending on the severity of the illness and how much care is required)
    - ☐ we'd expect one of our siblings to handle it
    - ☐ other ____

23. When your parents get older and require constant care, do you plan to have them live with you, if necessary?
    - ☐ yes
    - ☐ possibly, if there were no other alternatives
    - ☐ no, my husband wouldn't be able to deal with it
    - ☐ no, I wouldn't be able to deal with it
    - ☐ I don't know

24. When your husband's parents get older and require constant care, do you plan to have them live with you, if necessary?
    - ☐ yes
    - ☐ possibly, if there were no other alternatives
    - ☐ no, my husband wouldn't be able to deal with it
    - ☐ no, I wouldn't be able to deal with it
    - ☐ I don't know

Chapter 10

Backgrounds

Case Study

Denzel was overjoyed when he married Sharon, the daughter of Somali refugees who had fled persecution and famine. He could trace his own roots to that part of Africa, and delighted in learning about the customs and culture. Later, they moved to the same city as Sharon's large family. Denzel was looking forward to joining the thriving and active family culture, but it soon soured for him. "We spend every weekend with your folks," he said, "but I still feel like an outsider." Denzel continued, "Most of the time, they speak Somali and I don't even know what's going on."

QUIZ

1. Do you and your fiancé come from similar socio-economic backgrounds?
   - ☐ yes
   - ☐ somewhat
   - ☐ no

2. What type of socio-economic background were you raised in?
   - ☐ wealthy
   - ☐ well off
   - ☐ upper-middle class/professionals
   - ☐ middle class
   - ☐ working class
   - ☐ poverty line (e.g. on Government assistance)

3. In what socio-economic class do you expect to be once you are married?
   - ☐ wealthy
   - ☐ well off
   - ☐ upper-middle class/professionals
   - ☐ middle class
   - ☐ working class
   - ☐ poverty line (e.g. on Government assistance)

4. In what socio-economic class would you like to be five years from now?
   - ☐ wealthy
   - ☐ well off
   - ☐ upper-middle class/professionals
   - ☐ middle class
   - ☐ working class
   - ☐ poverty line (e.g. on Government assistance)
   - ☐ I don't care

5. Do you think you'll have trouble relating to friends or family from a different socio-economic background than your own?
   - ☐ none at all; I'm flexible
   - ☐ some, but I'll adjust
   - ☐ some, but I'll ignore the difficulties
   - ☐ a lot, but I won't see those family members or friends that often
   - ☐ a lot

6. Do you and your fiancé have similar education levels (e.g. high-school diploma or college degree)?
   - ☐ yes
   - ☐ no
   - ☐ somewhat (e.g. I have a degree from a community college, but he earned his at an "Ivy League" university)

7. If the two of you have different education levels, does the person with the higher level of education feel superior (e.g. that person has higher earning power) and the other inferior?
   - ☐ no, we are both intelligent adults; we are equal
   - ☐ yes, to a point (i.e. education can lead to a different way of thinking that is not transferable)
   - ☐ yes

Reading Tip

This book helps you pinpoint your issues as a couple; but you need to decide how to respond. For more reading tips, see the Introduction.

8. To whom, if anyone, are you politically affiliated?

The United States of America
☐ Republicans
☐ Democrats
☐ Independent parties
☐ no one—the whole political system is flawed
☐ I vote according to the platforms of the candidates, not by party

Canada
☐ Liberals
☐ Conservatives
☐ Alliance
☐ New Democrat Party
☐ Parti Quebecois
☐ Independent parties
☐ no one—the whole political system is flawed
☐ I vote according to the platforms of the candidates, not the party

9. Will your political differences (if any exist) cause friction in your home?
☐ no
☐ maybe, especially around elections
☐ yes

10. Do you and your fiancé come from similar ethnic/cultural backgrounds (e.g. Italian, Chinese, etc.)?
☐ yes
☐ there are very slight differences (e.g. an American marrying a person from Britain)
☐ somewhat (e.g. we were both born in the same country even though we have different ethnic origins)
☐ no

11. If your husband's family speaks a different language and does not know your language well, what would you do?
☐ I'd expect them to learn my language
☐ I'd try to learn their language just by being around them
☐ I'd take a crash course in their language
☐ I'd use gestures and sign language to convey my meaning
☐ I'd expect my husband to be with me whenever I'm in their company so he could translate

12. What do you think your husband would want you to do if you don't know his family's language?
    - ☐ he'd expect them to learn my language
    - ☐ he'd want me to try to learn their language just by being around them
    - ☐ he'd want me to take a crash course in their language
    - ☐ he'd be okay if I just used gestures and sign language to convey my meaning
    - ☐ he'd be okay with my needing him to be with me when I'm in their company so he could translate

13. If you come from different ethnic/cultural backgrounds and have children, which language (if different) would you choose to teach them?
    - ☐ English
    - ☐ my native language
    - ☐ my husband's native language
    - ☐ all languages spoken by the family

14. If you are not from the same ethnic/cultural background, how will you handle different customs?
    - ☐ I'll expect my husband to adopt my customs
    - ☐ I will adopt his customs
    - ☐ we will celebrate both traditions when possible
    - ☐ when two customs collide, we will alternate between mine and my husband's
    - ☐ we will adopt the customs of the country in which we live
    - ☐ we will not participate in any way in the other's customs

15. Do you expect to eat culturally specific food on a regular basis (e.g. haggis for Scottish, curry for Indians)?
    - ☐ yes, all the time
    - ☐ yes, several times a week
    - ☐ yes, once a week
    - ☐ yes, once or twice a month
    - ☐ yes, sometimes, such as when the family comes over or on special occasions
    - ☐ no

16. Do you think you should learn how to prepare your fiancé's culturally specific meals?
    - ☐ yes
    - ☐ yes, but he has to help me
    - ☐ no, he can cook for his family
    - ☐ no, it's too much work
    - ☐ no, I don't cook
    - ☐ no, there are no special foods connected to his culture

17. Are you aware that different cultural/ethnic backgrounds can have an impact on your finances (e.g. distinct cultures handle wedding presents and showers differently)?
    - ☐ yes
    - ☐ no
    - ☐ it's not relevant to our marriage

18. If you come from different ethnic/cultural backgrounds and have children, which customs will you adopt?
    - ☐ my husband's
    - ☐ mine
    - ☐ both traditions when possible
    - ☐ when two customs collide, we will alternate between mine and my husband's
    - ☐ we will make up new customs for our children
    - ☐ we will raise them with the customs of the country in which we currently live

19. When the two families get together (i.e. yours and your husband's), whose customs will take precedence?
    - ☐ both; we'll try to combine them
    - ☐ mine
    - ☐ my husband's
    - ☐ we'll make up new customs for the occasion

20. If you are not from the same ethnic/cultural background, how do you think your family and your husband's family will get along?
    - ☐ not well at all; we will keep them separate
    - ☐ not well, but they will have to adjust for the occasional family gathering
    - ☐ well enough
    - ☐ they will get along very well
    - ☐ they will get along great

Chapter 11

Religion

Case Study

Ramirez and Miriam met at college and had been married happily for several years. Ramirez had been raised in a Catholic family, and Miriam grew up in a Reformed Jewish household, but neither had attended religious services for years and they had never discussed their faith backgrounds. When their son was born, Ramirez was surprised that Miriam automatically arranged for a bris (circumcision) for their son. "If we have a bris," he argued, "I want him baptized, too." Each was surprised at the strength of their feelings.

QUIZ

1. Were you taught the teachings of a particular faith group or religious order as a child?
   - ☐ yes
   - ☐ no

2. If so, what religion was it?
   - ☐ born-again Christian
   - ☐ Christian
   - ☐ Mormon
   - ☐ Jehovah's Witness
   - ☐ Jewish
   - ☐ Islamic
   - ☐ Hindu
   - ☐ Baha'i
   - ☐ Buddhist
   - ☐ Sikh
   - ☐ Native Traditions
   - ☐ other ________________________________

3. Do you currently align yourself with any particular religion?
   - ☐ yes
   - ☐ no

Reading Tip

If your fiancé won't do the man's quiz, it's still worthwhile to do your quiz by yourself. For more reading tips, see the Introduction.

4. If yes, to what religion do you feel most closely connected?
   - ☐ born-again Christian
   - ☐ Christian
   - ☐ Mormon
   - ☐ Jehovah's Witness
   - ☐ Jewish
   - ☐ Islamic
   - ☐ Hindu
   - ☐ Baha'i
   - ☐ Buddhist
   - ☐ Sikh
   - ☐ Native Traditions
   - ☐ other ____________________

5. Where do you hope to get married?
   - ☐ in a Church
   - ☐ in a Mosque
   - ☐ in a Synagogue
   - ☐ in a Temple
   - ☐ outdoors
   - ☐ in a civil ceremony (e.g. city hall, backyard)
   - ☐ other ____________________
   - ☐ I don't care

6. Who do you want to perform your ceremony?
   - ☐ a Minister
   - ☐ a Priest
   - ☐ a Rabbi
   - ☐ a Mullah
   - ☐ a Guru
   - ☐ a Government official (e.g. a Judge)
   - ☐ other ____________________
   - ☐ I don't care

7. Do you think that faith and religion are the same thing?
   - ☐ yes
   - ☐ no
   - ☐ I'm not sure

8. How important is your faith (your particular beliefs) to you?
   - ☐ extremely
   - ☐ very
   - ☐ somewhat
   - ☐ not very
   - ☐ not at all

9. Do you pray?
   - ☐ yes, several times a day
   - ☐ yes, every day
   - ☐ yes, frequently
   - ☐ yes, when I need help
   - ☐ not usually
   - ☐ never

10. For the purposes of this survey, we'll be dealing with faith as demonstrated in religion. How close is your connection to your religion?
    - ☐ I closely adhere to the standards laid out by my religion (e.g. through the Bible, the Torah, or the Koran)
    - ☐ I try to live (in a general way) by the standards laid out by my religion
    - ☐ I'm only loosely connected to my religion, mostly out of habit
    - ☐ my faith is strong even though my connection to formal religion is weak
    - ☐ I attend services consistently
    - ☐ I attend services once in a while
    - ☐ I rarely attend services, perhaps only attending once or twice a year
    - ☐ I never attend services

11. If your religion is a central part of your life, do you think it's important that you and your husband are adherents of the same religion?
    - ☐ yes, we must be from exactly the same denomination or variety
    - ☐ yes, we must have very similar beliefs (e.g. both born-again Christians)
    - ☐ yes, we should belong to the same general religion; some similarity is necessary (e.g. a Catholic to a Protestant)
    - ☐ no, the person I marry is more important than religion
    - ☐ no

12. If you are not from the same religion and religion is important to you, how will you handle it?
    - ☐ I'll expect my husband to convert to my religion
    - ☐ I will convert to his religion
    - ☐ we will celebrate both religious customs and traditions when possible
    - ☐ when two religious traditions or customs collide, we will alternate between mine and my husband's
    - ☐ we will each remain true to our respective religions without expecting the other to participate in any way
    - ☐ I will continue with my own religion, because he does not have any religious affiliations or beliefs

13. If you attend services regularly, do you expect your husband to attend with you?
    - ☐ yes
    - ☐ only if he feels like it
    - ☐ no
    - ☐ we'll alternate between his services and mine, if he likes

14. Do you expect your level of participation in your religion to change after you get married?
    - ☐ it will increase
    - ☐ it will stay the same
    - ☐ it will decrease

15. Do you expect, on a regular basis, to eat food that is connected to your religious beliefs (e.g. Catholics traditionally eat fish on Fridays, Jews eat kosher food)?
    - ☐ yes, as specified by my religion
    - ☐ no
    - ☐ I'd like to, but it's not absolutely essential

16. Do you expect your husband to eat the same food, even if he doesn't belong to your faith?
    - ☐ yes
    - ☐ no
    - ☐ whatever he wants
    - ☐ I'd appreciate it, but I wouldn't insist

17. Do you think you should have to learn how to prepare your fiancé's religious meal requirements?
    - ☐ yes
    - ☐ yes, but he has to help
    - ☐ no, he should cook those meals
    - ☐ no, it's too much work
    - ☐ no, I don't cook
    - ☐ no, there are no special foods connected to his religion

18. If you come from different religions and have children, which religion will you choose to teach them?
    - ☐ mine
    - ☐ my husband's
    - ☐ both and then let them decide when they're old enough
    - ☐ all world religions and then they can decide when they're old enough
    - ☐ whatever one our child shows an interest in
    - ☐ none (we will not participate in any religion)

19. Will you expect your children to attend services, whether of your faith or your husband's?
    - ☐ yes
    - ☐ sometimes
    - ☐ no

20. Do you wish to send your child to a school with a particular religious orientation?
    - ☐ yes
    - ☐ maybe
    - ☐ no

21. If you choose to adopt your husband's religious views, how do you anticipate your parents and siblings, etc., will act when you or your child reaches a fundamental point in that religion (e.g. circumcision, confirmation, baptism)?
    - ☐ they will refuse to come
    - ☐ they will try to change our minds
    - ☐ they will come to the appropriate services, but they will not personally participate if it is against their consciences
    - ☐ we expect them to respect our choices and support us
    - ☐ they should fully immerse themselves in the tradition out of respect for us
    - ☐ other ________________________________

22. If your husband chooses to adopt your religious views, how do you anticipate his parents and siblings, etc., will act when he or your child reaches a fundamental point in that religion (e.g. circumcision, confirmation, baptism)?
    - ☐ they will refuse to come
    - ☐ they will try to change our minds
    - ☐ they will come to the appropriate services, but they will not personally participate if it is against their consciences
    - ☐ we expect them to respect our choices and support us
    - ☐ they should fully immerse themselves in the tradition out of respect for us
    - ☐ other ________________________________

For a chapter that is directed more towards Evangelical Christians, go to www.knowingme-knowingyou.com and download the chapter called "Faith" for free.

Chapter 12

Values

Case Study

Christine was looking forward to starting her new home-based business. She was delighted when she came down to her desk the first morning and found a brand new desk pen set, stapler, hole punch and two reams of bond paper. "You're so thoughtful! Thank you!" she told her husband Joseph. "It was nothing," he replied, explaining that he had "borrowed them on a permanent basis" from his office. Christine was shocked and started to cry. "What's the big deal? Everybody does it," he said. "You're not the man I married," she sobbed. "If you could cheat your boss, maybe you could cheat on me."

QUIZ

1. Of the various important issues in the world today, identify and rank the ones that are most important to you (1 being the most important).

	Rank
☐ the disparity between the rich and poor	____
☐ racial prejudice	____
☐ religious prejudice	____
☐ women's rights	____
☐ children's rights	____
☐ access to health care	____
☐ abortion	____
☐ crime	____
☐ the criminal justice system	____
☐ gun control	____
☐ the environment	____
☐ drinking and driving	____
☐ animal rights	____
☐ war	____
☐ other ________________________________	____

> **Reading Tip**
>
> Be honest! For more reading tips, see the Introduction.

2. Have you ever broken a promise?
   - ☐ yes, a major promise
   - ☐ yes, a little one
   - ☐ no

3. If yes, did you intend to break your promise?
   - ☐ yes
   - ☐ no
   - ☐ I'm not sure

4. Do you tend to make promises easily (e.g. I promise I'll get right on that)?
   - ☐ yes
   - ☐ no
   - ☐ I try not to, but sometimes they slip out
   - ☐ I'm very careful to only make promises I can keep

5. Do you usually keep your promises?
   - ☐ always
   - ☐ most of the time
   - ☐ some of the time
   - ☐ rarely
   - ☐ never

6. As an adult, have you ever cheated at anything?
   - ☐ yes, at sports
   - ☐ yes, in games of skill
   - ☐ yes, on my tax return
   - ☐ yes, on my college exams
   - ☐ yes, other ______________________________
   - ☐ no

7. Under what circumstances, if any, would you lie?
   - ☐ to spare someone's feelings
   - ☐ to ease a social situation
   - ☐ to protect someone I loved from hurt feelings
   - ☐ if my life or the life of someone else was threatened
   - ☐ to cover up something I or someone else should not have done
   - ☐ to advance my own goals (e.g. lying about my work history in order to get a job)
   - ☐ under no circumstances would I lie

8. How often do you lie?
   - ☐ never
   - ☐ rarely (once or twice a year)
   - ☐ sometimes (once or twice a month)
   - ☐ frequently (every day)
   - ☐ perpetually (several times a day)

9. What type of lie are you most likely to tell?
   - ☐ a social lie (e.g. saying someone looks wonderful when I privately think they look dreadful)
   - ☐ a straight-out lie (e.g. saying I know nothing about something that I actually participated in)
   - ☐ a large lie that leads to more lies (e.g. infidelity)
   - ☐ I lie without thinking because I want people to think well of me

10. To whom are you most likely to lie?
    - ☐ strangers
    - ☐ my boss
    - ☐ my family (e.g. my mother)
    - ☐ my husband
    - ☐ my children
    - ☐ no one

11. How important do you think honesty is in a marriage relationship?
    - ☐ extremely
    - ☐ somewhat (except when it will upset my husband)
    - ☐ not very (what he doesn't know won't hurt him)
    - ☐ not at all

12. If your husband is out late and tells you he's been working, what are you likely to think?
    - ☐ that he has been working
    - ☐ that he has been out with his buddies
    - ☐ that he has likely been up to something he doesn't want me to know about
    - ☐ that he is having an affair
    - ☐ it depends how often he calls saying he'll be late

13. Do you find it easy to trust?
    - ☐ yes, no one has really let me down before
    - ☐ yes, especially my fiancé because I know him so well
    - ☐ somewhat—it depends who it is I am asked to trust
    - ☐ I find it difficult to trust (I've been burned before)
    - ☐ I find it virtually impossible to trust
    - ☐ anyone who blindly trusts others is too naive

14. Are you a jealous person?
    - ☐ yes
    - ☐ sometimes
    - ☐ no
    - ☐ I'm not sure

15. Once you're married, do you think your husband will be a jealous person?
    - ☐ yes
    - ☐ sometimes
    - ☐ no
    - ☐ I'm not sure

16. If your husband were jealous of another man, how would you respond?
    - ☐ I'd laugh
    - ☐ I'd be flattered and enjoy the attention
    - ☐ I'd flirt just to see his reaction
    - ☐ I'd be annoyed that he doesn't trust me
    - ☐ I'd try not to do anything that would make him jealous

17. If you are jealous of another woman, how do you think your husband might respond?
    - ☐ he'd laugh
    - ☐ he'd be flattered and enjoy the attention
    - ☐ he'd flirt just to see my reaction
    - ☐ he'd be annoyed that I don't trust him
    - ☐ he'd try not to do anything that would make me jealous

18. How would you like your husband to respond when you are jealous?
    - ☐ I'd like him to ignore it (I know I can be a little possessive)
    - ☐ I'd like him to let me know that I'm the only one for him
    - ☐ I'd like him to compliment me and tell me all the reasons he loves me
    - ☐ I'd like him to try not to do anything that would make me jealous
    - ☐ other ____________________

19. Other than women, who or what else might make you jealous with respect to your husband?
    - ☐ his work
    - ☐ a hobby that takes up a lot of his time
    - ☐ friends who take him out a lot
    - ☐ his extended family (e.g. his parents, siblings)
    - ☐ our children
    - ☐ a pet
    - ☐ other ____________________

20. Have you ever stolen anything?
    - ☐ yes
    - ☐ no
    - ☐ when I was a child

21. Under what circumstances do you think it is okay to take something that doesn't belong to you?
    - ☐ under no circumstances
    - ☐ if someone left something at my house and forgot to get it, I'd keep it
    - ☐ I might take supplies from my employer (i.e. reasoning that they don't pay me enough anyway so I'm just taking what's rightfully mine)
    - ☐ I like to keep hotel towels or other items as souvenirs
    - ☐ I might take something in response to a dare
    - ☐ I do it to get a thrill
    - ☐ I might steal to put food on my family's table
    - ☐ other ______________________________

22. If someone were spreading rumors about your best friend, what would you do?
    - ☐ I'd tell them I don't want to hear it
    - ☐ I'd defend my friend
    - ☐ I'd beat the person up
    - ☐ I might join in on the gossip
    - ☐ I'd likely join in on the gossip
    - ☐ I'd tell my friend so she'd be prepared
    - ☐ I'd walk away

23. What would you tend to do if you are called to support a charity to which you have an emotional tie (e.g. breast cancer runs in your family)?
    - ☐ I'd talk it over with my husband
    - ☐ I'd probably offer to help any way I can
    - ☐ I'd canvass my neighborhood to raise support
    - ☐ I'd participate in some way other than monetary (e.g. volunteering to phone, walking to support the cause)
    - ☐ I'd give a large sum of money, but no time
    - ☐ I'd give a small sum of money, just to get them off my back
    - ☐ I'd say no way, but I'd feel guilty
    - ☐ I'd say no way
    - ☐ I'd hand the phone to my husband so he can say "no"

24. What would you tend to do if you are called to support a charity to which you <u>do not</u> have an emotional tie?
    - ☐ I'd talk it over with my husband
    - ☐ if I thought it was a good charity, I'd probably offer to help any way I can
    - ☐ I'd canvass my neighborhood to raise support
    - ☐ I'd participate in some way other than monetary (e.g. volunteering to phone, walking to support the cause)
    - ☐ I'd give a large sum of money, but no time
    - ☐ I'd give a small sum of money, just to get them off my back
    - ☐ I'd say no way, but I'd feel guilty
    - ☐ I'd say no way
    - ☐ I'd hand the phone to my husband so he can say "no"

25. How would you describe your work ethic (how you approach work)?
    - ☐ I approach my work wholeheartedly and always try to do the best I can
    - ☐ I'm a perfectionist; I like to do my work right, no matter how long it takes
    - ☐ if there is no one else to do the work, I'll do it even if I'm sick or it's a holiday
    - ☐ I do my work the best I can in the time I have available (i.e. I won't work overtime if I'm not paid)
    - ☐ work is a necessary evil
    - ☐ work is a waste of time
    - ☐ I work hard at my job, but I don't work hard at home (e.g. cleaning)

26. When you commit yourself to a project (whether at work, at home or in a club), how likely are you to quit before you're finished?
    - ☐ I would never quit
    - ☐ I likely would not quit
    - ☐ I might quit if the project was frustrating or lengthy
    - ☐ I might quit if it was interfering with my relationships (e.g. if I didn't have enough time with my husband)
    - ☐ I would probably lose interest

27. If you were asked to babysit for a family member or friend, what would you do?
    - ☐ I'd avoid it because I don't like children
    - ☐ I'd avoid it because I can't be bothered
    - ☐ I'd say sure and then forget the commitment and not show up
    - ☐ I'd say yes and be there as promised

28. How reliable are you?
    - ☐ very reliable
    - ☐ fairly reliable
    - ☐ it depends on what is being asked of me
    - ☐ not terribly reliable

29. Do you like to be punctual?
    - ☐ yes, definitely
    - ☐ yes, if I can
    - ☐ I try, but I always seem to be late
    - ☐ it's not that important to me
    - ☐ I could not care less

30. Do you smoke?
    - ☐ yes
    - ☐ no
    - ☐ sometimes
    - ☐ I used to

31. If you answered yes and if your fiancé objected to your smoking, would you try to give it up?
    - ☐ yes
    - ☐ my fiancé wouldn't ask me to do so
    - ☐ no, I like smoking

32. What types of alcoholic drinks do you most favor?
    - ☐ none
    - ☐ beer
    - ☐ wine
    - ☐ wine spritzers
    - ☐ cocktails/mixed drinks
    - ☐ hard liquor (e.g. whisky, vodka)
    - ☐ other ______________________

33. How often do you have a drink containing alcohol?
    - ☐ several times a day
    - ☐ every day
    - ☐ once or twice a week
    - ☐ once or twice a month (e.g. wine with a special dinner)
    - ☐ less than once or twice a month
    - ☐ I don't drink alcohol
    - ☐ I'm a recovering alcoholic

34. When you are drinking, how many drinks (or beers) do you tend to have at a time (e.g. over the space of an evening)?
    - ☐ 1
    - ☐ 2
    - ☐ 3
    - ☐ 4
    - ☐ 5
    - ☐ 5+

35. Have you ever driven while under the influence?
    - ☐ no
    - ☐ not that I know of
    - ☐ yes

36. At any time in the past, have you ever tried illegal drugs?
    - ☐ yes
    - ☐ no

37. If yes, what type of drugs have you tried?
    - ☐ marijuana
    - ☐ cocaine
    - ☐ heroin
    - ☐ crack
    - ☐ LSD/extasy/meth
    - ☐ other ______________________

38. Do your friends use drugs?
    - ☐ yes
    - ☐ some of them
    - ☐ no
    - ☐ not that I know of

39. Do you still use drugs?
    - ☐ yes
    - ☐ no
    - ☐ sometimes

40. Do you enjoy gambling?
    - ☐ yes, it's a lot of fun
    - ☐ yes, it adds extra spice to competition
    - ☐ yes, I enjoy playing poker with my friends
    - ☐ yes, I enjoy gambling on sports (my favorite team or my own sports ability)
    - ☐ yes, I love the glamour of casinos
    - ☐ I don't have anything against it, but I'm not really into it
    - ☐ no, I am opposed to gambling

41. How often do you gamble?
    - ☐ more frequently than once a week
    - ☐ once a week
    - ☐ twice a month
    - ☐ once a month
    - ☐ several times a year
    - ☐ once a year
    - ☐ once in a very long while (e.g. on a cruise ship vacation)
    - ☐ never

42. If you gamble, how much have you lost in one sitting?
    - ☐ $25 or less
    - ☐ $100 or less
    - ☐ $200 or less
    - ☐ $500 or less
    - ☐ $1,000 or less
    - ☐ $5,000 or less
    - ☐ $10,000 or less
    - ☐ more than $10,000

Chapter 13

Physical Appearance

Case Study

Roger was very concerned and supportive during his wife Emily's pregnancy. He even gained fifteen pounds himself. After their twins were born, he gave up his twice weekly tennis games to help Emily keep up with the infants. While Emily worked hard to regain her figure though, Roger continued to gain weight. Roger noticed that she did not seem to respond when he wanted to be romantic. "Is it the twins?" he asked. "It's partly that," she replied, "but I also have to admit your spare tire isn't exactly a turn on."

QUIZ

1. How important do you think it is that you look attractive (e.g. well groomed and dressed)?
   - ☐ it's extremely important
   - ☐ it's important
   - ☐ it's important only when I'm working or at an occasion (e.g. party)
   - ☐ it's not terribly important
   - ☐ it's not important at all

2. How important is it to you that your fiancé look attractive?
   - ☐ it's extremely important
   - ☐ it's important
   - ☐ it's important only when he's working or at an occasion (e.g. party)
   - ☐ it's not terribly important
   - ☐ it's not important at all

3. Do you have the same standards of grooming for yourself as for your fiancé?
   - ☐ yes
   - ☐ no, I expect my fiancé to be more well groomed
   - ☐ no, I expect my fiancé to be less well groomed

4. How much time do you spend every day achieving a certain "look" that you think is attractive (e.g. applying make up, fixing hair)?
   - ☐ 5 minutes
   - ☐ 15 minutes
   - ☐ 30 minutes
   - ☐ an hour
   - ☐ more than an hour

5. How much time would you be willing to spend waiting for your husband to achieve a certain look?
   - ☐ 5 minutes
   - ☐ 15 minutes
   - ☐ 30 minutes
   - ☐ an hour
   - ☐ more than an hour

6. Do you intend to buy your husband's clothes so your preferences are guaranteed?
   - ☐ definitely
   - ☐ likely
   - ☐ once in a while
   - ☐ only if he asks me to do so
   - ☐ never

Reading Tip

Fill out the quiz on your own, without consulting your fiancé until you've finished each chapter. For more reading tips, see the Introduction.

7. Do you intend to select what your husband wears to given events (e.g. an important meeting, a wedding)?
   - ☐ definitely
   - ☐ likely
   - ☐ once in a while
   - ☐ only if he asks me to do so
   - ☐ never

8. Once you're married, do you intend to shave your legs regularly?
   - ☐ yes
   - ☐ only in the summer
   - ☐ only if I'm wearing something that shows my legs (e.g. party dress)
   - ☐ yes, especially before we make love
   - ☐ if my husband wants me to do so
   - ☐ no

9. Once you're married, do you intend to shave your underarms regularly?
   - ☐ yes
   - ☐ only in the summer
   - ☐ only if I'm wearing something that shows my underarms (e.g. party dress)
   - ☐ yes, especially before we make love
   - ☐ if my husband wants me to do so
   - ☐ no

10. How would you feel if your husband grew a moustache?
    - ☐ great (he already has one)
    - ☐ I think it would be attractive
    - ☐ I wouldn't mind, as long as he keeps it neat (addressed in chapter 13, question 11 of the man's quiz)
    - ☐ I'd be okay with it
    - ☐ I wouldn't like it
    - ☐ I'd hate it and insist he shave
    - ☐ I wouldn't like how it feels to kiss him
    - ☐ I don't care one way or the other

11. How would you feel if your husband grew a beard?
    - ☐ great (he already has one)
    - ☐ I think it would be attractive
    - ☐ I wouldn't mind, as long as he keeps it neat (addressed in chapter 13, question 11 of the man's quiz)
    - ☐ I'd be okay with it
    - ☐ I wouldn't like it
    - ☐ I'd hate it and insist he shave
    - ☐ I wouldn't like how it feels to kiss him
    - ☐ I don't care one way or the other

12. If your husband were clean-shaven, how often would you expect him to shave?
    - ☐ twice a day
    - ☐ once a day
    - ☐ as often as he needs to in order to look neat
    - ☐ as often as he needs to so he doesn't scratch me when he kisses me
    - ☐ twice a week
    - ☐ once a week
    - ☐ I wouldn't care
    - ☐ I think it feels sexy when his face is a bit scratchy

13. If you noticed an offensive odor coming from your husband, what would you do?
    - ☐ I'd ignore it
    - ☐ I'd ignore it, but I'd refuse to get close to him
    - ☐ I'd gently hint that he needs to take a shower or brush his teeth
    - ☐ I'd tell him what I'm smelling (i.e. that he stinks) and ask him to correct it

14. If you believed that you were becoming less attractive, to what level would you go to retain your looks?
    - ☐ I'd buy more cosmetics/moisturizers
    - ☐ I'd diet
    - ☐ I'd exercise more regularly
    - ☐ I'd dye my hair
    - ☐ I'd save up for spa treatments
    - ☐ I'd try herbal treatments (e.g. cucumbers on the eyes)
    - ☐ I'd wear uncomfortable undergarments like a girdle or underwire bra
    - ☐ I'd undergo lipo suction
    - ☐ I'd have cosmetic surgery
    - ☐ I'd do all of the above
    - ☐ I wouldn't do anything
    - ☐ other ____________________

15. Would the cost make a difference with respect to what you do to look attractive?
    - ☐ yes
    - ☐ no, I'd want to cut back in other spending to pay for this
    - ☐ no, I don't care how much it costs
    - ☐ no, not if we have the money

16. If you were to gain weight, would it affect your perception of your attractiveness?
    - ☐ yes
    - ☐ no
    - ☐ it depends on how much weight I gained
    - ☐ I am going to work hard to ensure I don't gain weight

17. If you gain more weight than you would like, what would you do?
    - ☐ I wouldn't do anything
    - ☐ I'd try to lose weight by buying exercise equipment or by signing up to a gym
    - ☐ I'd ask my husband to join a fitness club so we could help each other stay in shape
    - ☐ I'd diet
    - ☐ I'd cook foods appropriate for my diet
    - ☐ I'd make sure there were no snacks in the house
    - ☐ I'd pin a picture on the fridge of me looking fat
    - ☐ other ____________________

18. If your husband were to gain weight, would it affect how attractive you find him?
    - ☐ yes
    - ☐ no
    - ☐ it depends on how much weight he gained
    - ☐ I hope he doesn't gain any weight

19. If your husband gains more weight than you would like, what would you do?
    - ☐ I wouldn't do anything
    - ☐ I'd nag him every day to lose weight
    - ☐ I'd encourage him to lose weight by buying him exercise equipment or by signing him up to a gym
    - ☐ I'd sign up with him to go to a fitness club so we could help each other stay in shape
    - ☐ I'd encourage him to diet
    - ☐ I'd eat or cook foods appropriate for his diet
    - ☐ I'd make sure there were no snacks in the house
    - ☐ I'd comment favorably on the attractiveness of men more slim than he is
    - ☐ I'd make insulting comments about his weight
    - ☐ I'd pin a picture on the fridge of him looking fat
    - ☐ other ______________________________

20. If your husband were to go bald, would you find him less attractive?
    - ☐ no, I find bald men attractive
    - ☐ no, I don't care if he goes bald
    - ☐ maybe
    - ☐ definitely

21. If he were to go bald, what would you expect him to do?
    - ☐ nothing
    - ☐ cover his bald spot with a long flap of hair
    - ☐ buy a hair piece
    - ☐ use a special shampoo to slow baldness
    - ☐ use medications like Rogaine
    - ☐ undergo hair surgery of some sort, like hair plugs

Chapter 14

In Sickness and In Health

Case Study

Carol and Malcolm (the authors) were married ten years when Carol, then in her mid-thirties, was diagnosed with a debilitating medical condition called Fibromyalgia. While this condition was not life threatening, she was in extreme pain every minute of every day. Traditional medicine could do little. Their world was turned upside down—financially, emotionally and physically. Carol suffered from doubts about her usefulness as a wife and mother. Every day was a challenge for her, and Malcolm struggled to help in any way he could even as he watched his wife's personality change and her energy disappear. One day, as Carol crawled up the stairs on her hands and knees, unable to find the strength to climb them any other way, their three-year-old daughter Deanna cried out, "Let me help you up the stairs, Mommy." During this difficult time, Carol and Malcolm's commitment to love each other "in sickness and in health" was severely tested.

QUIZ

1. How important is it to you that you remain healthy?
   - ☐ extremely important
   - ☐ very important
   - ☐ important
   - ☐ not too important
   - ☐ I'll worry about my health later

2. Is it likely that you will worry about your husband's health?
   - ☐ yes
   - ☐ no
   - ☐ only if he develops problems of some sort

3. Do you follow a specialized diet that you would like your husband to adopt?
   - ☐ no, I'm not on a special diet
   - ☐ yes, my diet is regulated by my religion
   - ☐ yes, I have food allergies
   - ☐ yes, I'm a vegetarian
   - ☐ yes, I need to lose weight to be healthy
   - ☐ yes, I can't digest dairy products
   - ☐ yes, I won't eat refined sugar
   - ☐ yes, I need a special diet, but my husband doesn't need to eat like I do

4. If your husband required a special diet, would you be willing to eat the same foods as him?
   - ☐ yes
   - ☐ no
   - ☐ it would depend on the diet

5. Do you take vitamins or supplements?
   - ☐ yes
   - ☐ no
   - ☐ only when I feel ill (e.g. echinacea, zinc lozenges)

6. Do you believe in getting regular exercise?
   - ☐ yes
   - ☐ no
   - ☐ if I can work it into my schedule

7. What type of exercise do you tend to do most?
   - ☐ competitive sports (e.g. tennis, hockey, baseball)
   - ☐ jogging
   - ☐ weight lifting
   - ☐ aerobics
   - ☐ walking
   - ☐ stretching
   - ☐ sex
   - ☐ other ______________________________

8. How often do you exercise?
   - ☐ every day
   - ☐ three times a week
   - ☐ twice a week
   - ☐ once a week
   - ☐ twice a month
   - ☐ once a month
   - ☐ less frequently than once a month

Reading Tip

Answer based on how you feel now, not how you think you'll feel in the future. For more reading tips, see the Introduction.

9. How long do you typically exercise each time?
    - ☐ 15 minutes or less
    - ☐ 30 minutes or less
    - ☐ 45 minutes or less
    - ☐ 1 hour or less
    - ☐ 2 hours or less
    - ☐ 3 hours or less
    - ☐ more than 3 hours

10. Once you're married, would you prefer to exercise with your husband or alone?
    - ☐ with my husband (e.g. hiking, tennis)
    - ☐ alone (e.g. jogging, weight training)
    - ☐ both (e.g. aerobics one day, tennis the next)

11. If your husband couldn't lift you up in his arms (i.e. sweep you off your feet), what would you do?
    - ☐ I'd laugh at the situation
    - ☐ I'd think he was a weakling
    - ☐ I'd insist that he begin weight training
    - ☐ I'd be embarrassed about my weight
    - ☐ I'd be turned off because he isn't "manly" enough
    - ☐ I wouldn't care

12. If you catch a bad cold or flu, how do you tend to act?
    - ☐ I pretend I'm not sick, even to myself
    - ☐ I don't let anyone know I don't feel well, because I think it's a sign of weakness
    - ☐ I immediately begin taking home remedies to try to head it off (e.g. I take garlic, zinc lozenges)
    - ☐ I take over-the-counter medicine
    - ☐ I complain a lot
    - ☐ I go to bed
    - ☐ I go to the doctor and follow his/her instructions
    - ☐ I take prescribed medicine, if the doctor orders it, but as soon as I start feeling better, I stop taking it

13. When you are sick with the flu or a cold, how would you like your husband to treat you?
    - ☐ he should leave me alone
    - ☐ he should spoil me (e.g. bring me tissues, make chicken noodle soup)
    - ☐ he should treat me exactly the same as when I'm well
    - ☐ other ____________________

14. If your husband gets sick, what would be your first reaction?
    - □ I'd tell him to shake it off
    - □ I'd tell him to ignore it
    - □ I'd ask him if he would like me to do anything for him
    - □ I'd fuss over him (e.g. I'd insist he go to bed)
    - □ I'd leave him alone
    - □ I would be afraid I'd catch it, so I'd avoid him
    - □ I wouldn't treat him any differently

15. If you got sick for an extended period of time (e.g. several months) with a serious illness (e.g. Postpartum Depression, recovery from surgery of some kind), how would you like your husband to treat you?
    - □ he should treat me exactly the same as before
    - □ I'd like him to leave me alone
    - □ he should care, but not say much
    - □ I'd like him to listen to me vent my frustrations and anxiety, and he should sympathize
    - □ he should spoil me, trying to meet my every need and desire
    - □ if special care was needed (e.g. following surgery), I'd expect him to do whatever he had to do to help me
    - □ I'd expect him to hire suitable help (e.g. a maid, a nurse) until I'm better
    - □ I'd like him to call in a family member to help

16. If your husband got sick for an extended period of time, how would you treat him?
    - □ I'd treat him exactly the same as before
    - □ I'd leave him alone
    - □ I'd care, but I wouldn't say much
    - □ I'd listen to him vent his frustrations and anxiety, and I'd sympathize
    - □ I'd spoil him, trying to meet his every need and desire
    - □ if special care was needed (e.g. following surgery), I'd do whatever I had to do to help him
    - □ I'd hire suitable help (e.g. a nurse, a yard service) until he got better
    - □ I'd call in a family member to help
    - □ I'd avoid him

17. If your husband was diagnosed with a permanent medical condition (e.g. MS, arthritis), how do you think you'd respond?
    - □ I'd like to think I'd stick with him come what may
    - □ I'd pray
    - □ I'd be very angry at life
    - □ I'd get depressed
    - □ I would suggest counseling for both of us
    - □ I'd have an affair
    - □ I'd consider leaving him

18. If you were diagnosed with a permanent medical condition (e.g. MS, arthritis), how would you feel and how would it affect your relationship with your husband?
    - ☐ I'd feel like a failure as a wife
    - ☐ I'd probably suggest that my husband leave me for someone better
    - ☐ I'd expect him to hang in there with me
    - ☐ I'd be depressed and I'd need his support
    - ☐ I'd be angry at life and I'd need his encouragement
    - ☐ I'd be angry at life and I'd push him away
    - ☐ I'd ask him to go with me for counselling
    - ☐ I'd accept it and I'd expect my husband to do so as well
    - ☐ other ______________________________

19. Does your family have a history of a serious health problem (e.g. mental illness, Huntington's Disease, breast cancer at an early age)?
    - ☐ yes
    - ☐ not that I know of, but we should look into it
    - ☐ no

20. If yes, what is the health problem?
    - ☐ mental illness
    - ☐ genetic problems
    - ☐ predisposition to cancer
    - ☐ predisposition to heart disease
    - ☐ other ______________________________

21. Would this change how you feel about having children?
    - ☐ yes
    - ☐ maybe
    - ☐ no

Chapter 15

Divorce and Re-Marriage

Case Study

Marianne and Jonah were engaged and happily planning their wedding. Marianne was working on planning the ceremony and vows when Jonah brought up the subject of a prenuptial agreement. Marianne was shocked. "How can you even think of such a thing? I thought it was going to be until death do us part," she protested. "A prenuptial agreement means you are thinking we could end up divorced! Why bother getting married and vowing to love each other forever?"

QUIZ

1. Do you come from a divorced home?
   - ☐ yes
   - ☐ no

2. If yes, how did it affect you?
   - ☐ I was okay with it
   - ☐ I knew my parents both loved me, so I was okay
   - ☐ I felt torn loyalties between my Mom and Dad
   - ☐ my parents used me as a pawn
   - ☐ I was angry
   - ☐ I was hurt
   - ☐ I thought I was to blame

3. Do you believe that divorce is ever right?
   - ☐ yes
   - ☐ yes, if one or both partners fall out of love
   - ☐ yes, if there is a lot of tension in the marriage
   - ☐ yes, if one partner or children are being physically abused
   - ☐ yes, if one partner or children are being emotionally abused
   - ☐ yes, if one partner is unfaithful sexually
   - ☐ only after marriage counseling has been tried
   - ☐ only as a last resort
   - ☐ I'm not sure
   - ☐ not for me
   - ☐ never
   - ☐ I wouldn't presume to judge

Reading Tip

This quiz is designed to be non-judgmental, so relax. For more reading tips, see the Introduction.

4. Do you want your husband to sign a prenuptial agreement?
   - ☐ yes
   - ☐ no

5. Have you ever been divorced?
   - ☐ yes
   - ☐ no
   - ☐ I'm in the process of getting a divorce

6. If yes, how do you feel about your divorce?
   - ☐ okay; my ex-husband and I are still friends
   - ☐ we were too young
   - ☐ it happens
   - ☐ it's over and I don't want to discuss it
   - ☐ it was the best solution to an unfortunate situation
   - ☐ I feel like I failed
   - ☐ I had to get out for health reasons (e.g. abused, mental anguish)
   - ☐ I was devastated
   - ☐ he was a jerk and I'm better off without him

7. Do you have children from your first marriage?
   - ☐ yes, I have sole custody
   - ☐ yes, and I share custody with my ex-husband
   - ☐ yes, but I do not have custody
   - ☐ no
   - ☐ **if both you and your fiancé answered "no" to this question, you can skip to the next chapter**

8. If you have children from your first marriage, how important is it to you for them to like your future husband?
    - ☐ it's absolutely essential
    - ☐ it's important, but I have the right to decide
    - ☐ it would be nice
    - ☐ it's not terribly important (after all, I'm the one marrying him)
    - ☐ it's not important (I deserve a chance at happiness; they will grow to like him in time)

9. Do you expect them to call him Dad?
    - ☐ yes
    - ☐ no
    - ☐ it's up to them
    - ☐ eventually

10. If your fiancé has children from his first marriage, how important is it to you that they like you?
    - ☐ it's absolutely essential
    - ☐ it's important
    - ☐ it would be nice
    - ☐ it's not terribly important (after all, I'm marrying him, not them)
    - ☐ it's not important (I deserve a chance at happiness; they will grow to like me in time)

11. Do you expect them to call you Mom?
    - ☐ yes
    - ☐ no
    - ☐ it's up to them
    - ☐ eventually

12. What concerns you most about taking care of your husband's child(ren) from a previous marriage?
    - ☐ whether I have any authority and whether that authority will be challenged by the child or by my husband
    - ☐ the child's health (e.g. does he/she have allergies to food or medicine)
    - ☐ making sure good, well-balanced meals are served and eaten
    - ☐ establishing and enforcing bedtime routines and times, or, for older children, curfews
    - ☐ making the child keep up adequate hygiene (e.g. brushing teeth, showers)
    - ☐ making the child follow rules of tidiness in my home (e.g. cleaning up after himself/herself)
    - ☐ making sure the child does his/her homework
    - ☐ making sure that the child gets to the various clubs or commitments he/she may have
    - ☐ whether the child will try to sabotage my relationship with my husband
    - ☐ other ______________________________

13. How would you handle differences in routines and habits between your home and the home of your child's other parent(s)?
    - ☐ we'd all work together (me, my husband, the child's natural father and his current wife if he has one) to try to agree to some rules that will then be common to both households
    - ☐ we'd call the other parent as a problematic situation arises (e.g. the child refuses to eat)
    - ☐ we'd try to establish our own rules even though they aren't respected by the child's other parent(s)
    - ☐ we'd have a "This is my house and while you're under my roof, you'll obey me" rule
    - ☐ there would <u>not</u> be a lot of rules in our house

14. If you have a child from your previous relationship, how would you handle the issue of authority over the him/her?
    - ☐ my ex-husband and I would jointly make important decisions regarding the child
    - ☐ my ex-husband, my current husband and I would jointly make important decisions regarding the child
    - ☐ my current husband and I would jointly make important decisions regarding the child, even though my husband is not his/her natural father
    - ☐ I would make the decisions about the child, but I'd ask for my husband's advice
    - ☐ I would be the only one responsible for making decisions regarding my child
    - ☐ I would have the final say when it comes to dealing with my child
    - ☐ if I am not at home, my husband would have complete authority over the child (e.g. when an immediate response is required)

15. If your husband has a child from his previous relationship, how would you handle the issue of authority over his child?
    - ☐ I think the decision about how to handle the child should be arrived at by my husband and his ex-wife
    - ☐ I think the decision should involve my husband, the child's natural mother and me
    - ☐ I would expect to make decisions jointly with my current husband, even though I am not the child's natural mother
    - ☐ my husband should make the decisions about his child, but I'd like him to ask for my advice
    - ☐ my husband would be the only one responsible for making decisions regarding his child
    - ☐ my husband would have the final say when it comes to dealing with his child
    - ☐ if my husband is not at home, I would want complete authority over the child (e.g. when an immediate response is required)

16. If a confrontation occurred between your child from a previous marriage and your husband, how would you respond?
    - ☐ I'd hear them both out, decide what I personally believe about the situation and tell them
    - ☐ I'd side with my husband because I want to present a unified front to the child
    - ☐ I'd side with my child because he/she is having a difficult time adjusting to my new relationship
    - ☐ I'd argue both sides to get them to talk it out
    - ☐ I'd attempt to mediate
    - ☐ I'd walk away and let them sort it out
    - ☐ I don't know what I'd do

17. If a confrontation occurred between your child from your previous marriage and your husband's child from his previous marriage, how would you respond?
    - ☐ I'd hear them both out, decide what I personally believe about the situation and tell them
    - ☐ I'd side with my child, because I know him/her well enough to know if he/she is being fair or honest
    - ☐ I'd wait for my husband to be present, so we could sort it out together
    - ☐ I'd argue both sides to get them to talk it out
    - ☐ I'd attempt to mediate
    - ☐ I'd walk away and let them sort it out
    - ☐ I don't know what I'd do

18. In the case of divorce, if children are given in custody to only one parent, do you think the grandparents of the non-custodial side should have the right to see their grandchildren?
    - ☐ yes
    - ☐ yes, under supervision
    - ☐ no
    - ☐ it depends ____

Chapter 16

Friends

Case Study

Monica and Daphne were good friends, and shared everything. When they each married, however, things started to fall apart. Monica's husband Alan, a computer programmer, and Daphne's husband Mike, a high school gym teacher, couldn't stand each other. Mike thought Alan was a "nerdy" bore, and Alan thought Mike was irresponsible and immature. After a few barbecues and a vacation together, Monica noticed that Alan became depressed and grumpy every time an event with Daphne and Mike was coming up. Monica got angry with him. "Why should I have to give up my friendship with Daphne?" she asked. "Why should I have to put up with Mike's practical jokes?" Alan responded. "Just go over there and leave me out of it."

QUIZ

1. Once you're married, how often do you expect to see your friends, independent of your husband?
   - ☐ every day
   - ☐ once or twice a week
   - ☐ once or twice a month
   - ☐ a few times a year
   - ☐ never

2. Do you see yourself hanging out more with friends who are also married or who are in a serious relationship?
   - ☐ yes
   - ☐ no
   - ☐ we'll see

3. Do you expect to maintain close relationships with friends who are not married?
   - ☐ yes
   - ☐ probably
   - ☐ I hope so
   - ☐ no

Reading Tip

If your answer is not listed, write it in the margin. For more reading tips, see the Introduction.

4. Would you do the same type of activities (for singles) that you used to do with your friends before you were married (e.g. go to bars, go clubbing, watch male strippers)?
   - ☐ yes
   - ☐ only if they were appropriate for a married woman (e.g. shopping)
   - ☐ I didn't do those things when I was unattached, so I wouldn't do them when I'm married
   - ☐ no

5. How will you blend your single friends and your married state?
   - ☐ I'll get together with my friends for breakfast or lunch so as not to interfere with my husband's schedule
   - ☐ I'll invite my friends to our house where we'll entertain them together
   - ☐ I'll invite them over when my husband is out of town or busy
   - ☐ I'll go out for an evening with my friends
   - ☐ I'll stay in touch by phone or e-mail
   - ☐ I will no longer keep these friendships

6. What would you do if your husband doesn't like your best friend?
   - ☐ I'd let my friend know how my husband feels even if it jeopardizes the friendship
   - ☐ I'd let my friend know how he feels and avoid putting them together (e.g. I'd get together alone with her for lunch)
   - ☐ I wouldn't let on to my friend, but I'd try to see her alone whenever possible
   - ☐ I would insist that my husband accept her and put up with her when we're together
   - ☐ I would no longer keep her as a close friend

7. What would you do if your best friend doesn't like your husband?
   - ☐ my husband comes first, so I would no longer keep her as a close friend
   - ☐ I'd let my husband know how my friend feels and see what he says
   - ☐ I'd let my husband know how my friend feels and avoid putting them together
   - ☐ I wouldn't let on to my husband, but I'd try to see my friend alone whenever possible
   - ☐ I would insist that my friend accept my husband and put up with him when we're together

8. What would you do if your best friend married someone your husband can't stand?
   - ☐ I'd let my friend know how my husband feels even if it jeopardizes the friendship
   - ☐ I'd let my friend know how he feels and avoid putting the men together (e.g. I'd get together with only her for lunch)
   - ☐ I wouldn't let on, but I'd try to see my friend alone whenever possible
   - ☐ I would insist that my husband accept my friend's husband and put up with him when we're together
   - ☐ we would stop being friends with them

9. Are there couples that you know where all of you get along well (i.e. both you and your fiancé enjoy their company)?
   - ☐ yes
   - ☐ not yet, but we'll likely connect with somebody once we're married
   - ☐ no

10. If yes, how would you feel about spending vacations with your friends?
    - ☐ I'd love to vacation with them, all the time
    - ☐ I'd love to vacation with them, some of the time
    - ☐ we could share a room while on vacation
    - ☐ I'd love to vacation with them as long as we have separate rooms
    - ☐ I'd prefer to vacation without our friends

11. Couples who are friends (men and women all get along) may express their friendship in different ways. Which of the following expressions of friendship between you and your male friend would make you uncomfortable?
    - ☐ if he hugged me
    - ☐ if he kissed me (e.g. under the mistletoe or at New Year's)
    - ☐ if he gave me a lingering kiss
    - ☐ if he held me very close while dancing
    - ☐ if he touched me a lot
    - ☐ if he put his arm around me
    - ☐ other ____________________

12. Which of the following expressions of friendship between your husband and a female friend would make you uncomfortable?
    - ☐ if she hugged him
    - ☐ if she kissed him (e.g. under the mistletoe or at New Year's)
    - ☐ if she gave him a lingering kiss
    - ☐ if she held him very close while dancing
    - ☐ if she touched him a lot
    - ☐ if she put her arm around him
    - ☐ if my husband hugged her
    - ☐ if he kissed her
    - ☐ if he held her close while dancing
    - ☐ if he touched her a lot
    - ☐ if he put his arm around her
    - ☐ other ______________________________

13. Would you ever want to go out with a male friend?
    - ☐ yes
    - ☐ yes, but only if he is a friend of my husband's as well (e.g. he's filling in for my husband at a function my husband can't attend)
    - ☐ yes, but only if my husband came, too
    - ☐ no

14. How would you <u>like</u> your husband to react if you proposed an outing alone with a male friend?
    - ☐ he should trust me and let me go with no objections
    - ☐ he should let me go, but let me know how he feels about it
    - ☐ he should object, but let me decide (it's nice that he cares enough to be jealous)
    - ☐ he should be so jealous he tells me not to go (he would forbid it)
    - ☐ it would depend on where we were going and what we'd be doing

15. How do you think your fiancé would, in reality, respond to that idea?
    - ☐ he would trust me and let me go with no objections
    - ☐ he would let me go, but let me know how he feels about it
    - ☐ he would object, but let me decide
    - ☐ he would secretly follow me to make sure nothing inappropriate happens
    - ☐ he would come up with any excuse he could think of to interrupt my time with my friend
    - ☐ he would be extremely jealous and tell me, if I love him, I wouldn't go
    - ☐ he would tell me not to go (he'd forbid it)
    - ☐ it would depend on where we were going and what we'd be doing

16. Would your husband be willing to go out with you and one of your male friends?
    - ☐ yes
    - ☐ no
    - ☐ I don't know

17. If your husband wanted to go out alone with a female friend, how would you respond to the idea?
    - ☐ I would trust him and let him go with no objections
    - ☐ I would let him go, but let him know how I feel about it
    - ☐ I would object, but I'd let him decide whether to go or not
    - ☐ I would secretly follow them to make sure nothing inappropriate happens
    - ☐ I would come up with any excuse I could think of to interrupt their time together
    - ☐ I would be extremely jealous and tell him, if he loves me, he wouldn't go
    - ☐ I would tell him not to go (I'd forbid it)
    - ☐ my reaction would depend on where they were going and what they'd be doing

18. Would you be willing to go along with your husband if he goes out with a female friend?
    - ☐ yes
    - ☐ no
    - ☐ I'm not sure

Chapter 17

Grief

Case Study

Walter and Eileen met and married when they were both in their late thirties. They were anxious to start a family and were extremely pleased when Eileen became pregnant after two years of trying. Tragically, their son was born with an inoperable heart defect and died six days after he was born.

Eileen's grief consumed her—it was all she could think about. She needed to talk about her feelings all the time. Walter felt extremely angry—too angry to talk about it. When Eileen poured out her feelings to him, it brought out his anger and they argued constantly. After three months, they decided to separate while seeking counseling.

The counselor understood their different ways of grieving and advised Eileen to talk about her feelings with a sympathetic friend. Walter was encouraged to join a karate club, where he could work out his anger in a controlled environment until he could deal with his feelings. After three months, they reconciled and soon afterwards became parents of twin girls.

QUIZ

1. Have you experienced a significant loss (e.g. loss of a parent, a romantic break up)?
   - ☐ yes
   - ☐ no

2. There are many types of grief. When we lose a job, break off a relationship, or lose a pet, we may grieve. As far as you can tell, when grieving, what is your first response?
   - ☐ I really don't know since I've never really experienced grief
   - ☐ I withdraw from others (e.g. lick my wounds in private)
   - ☐ I cry
   - ☐ I pretend nothing has happened and bottle it up inside
   - ☐ I get angry
   - ☐ I need to talk about the experience many times
   - ☐ other ________________

3. How would you like your husband to respond when you are experiencing grief?
   - ☐ I'd want him to leave me alone
   - ☐ I'd want him to put up with my bad mood, but otherwise not worry about it
   - ☐ I'd like his constant attention
   - ☐ I'd like him to listen to me express my grief and let me cry on his shoulder
   - ☐ I'd like frequent physical expressions of comfort, such as a hug
   - ☐ I'd want him to be patient
   - ☐ I'd like him to take over some of my chores so my overall load is lightened
   - ☐ other ________________

4. Other than for your husband, for whom or what would you grieve significantly (i.e. enough to affect your day-to-day emotions or routines)?
   - ☐ the loss of family relationships due to discord
   - ☐ a miscarriage
   - ☐ the death of my child
   - ☐ the death of my mother
   - ☐ the death of my father
   - ☐ the death of my grandmother
   - ☐ the death of my grandfather
   - ☐ the death of a brother/sister
   - ☐ the death of a pet
   - ☐ the loss of a job or career
   - ☐ the loss of personal possessions (e.g. in a fire)
   - ☐ other ________________

Reading Tip

This book helps you pinpoint your issues as a couple; but you need to decide how to respond. For more reading tips, see the Introduction.

5. Do you understand that your husband may grieve over different things than you and would you support him accordingly?
   - ☐ yes
   - ☐ no
   - ☐ I don't know

6. Would you be willing to seek help (i.e. counseling) when you are grief-stricken?
   - ☐ yes
   - ☐ probably
   - ☐ I'm not sure
   - ☐ no

7. Would you support your husband if he needed counseling to handle his grief?
   - ☐ yes
   - ☐ probably
   - ☐ I'm not sure
   - ☐ no

Chapter 18

Previous Romances

Case Study

Joey and Rhonda were visiting Rhonda's hometown on the other side of the country for the first time since they were married the previous year. While shopping at the neighborhood mall, Joey was surprised to come out of an electronics store and find Rhonda engaged in a conversation with another man. Just as Joey walked up, Rhonda and the other man hugged and the stranger left. Joey was surprised that Rhonda didn't introduce them. Later, he was chatting with Rhonda's mom and mentioned what had happened. "Oh, that must have been Richard," she told him. "He and Rhonda dated for over three years. I thought they would get married." Later Joey confronted Rhonda. "You must still have feelings for him!"

QUIZ

1. Would you want to know about your fiancé's previous romances?
   - ☐ yes
   - ☐ no (i.e. what I don't know won't hurt me)
   - ☐ I'm not sure
   - ☐ I would only want to know about any girlfriends with whom he was serious

2. If you want to know about a previous relationship, how much detail do you want?
   - ☐ I want to know her name and how long they were involved
   - ☐ I want to know what she looked like
   - ☐ I want to know how serious the relationship got
   - ☐ I want to know whether they slept together
   - ☐ I want to know who broke up with whom and why
   - ☐ I want to know how I compare to her
   - ☐ I want to be reassured that I am better for my fiancé than she was
   - ☐ not much; I'd rather just get a general idea of what girlfriends were in his past without any details
   - ☐ I don't want to know

3. If your fiancé refused to provide you with the information you wanted about his past romances, what would you do?
   - ☐ I'd respect his wishes, figuring it is all in the past
   - ☐ I'd question his family and friends when he's not around
   - ☐ I'd continue to question him when there's an opportunity
   - ☐ I'd wait nervously to meet one of his ex-girlfriends (or ex-wives) at some point in the future
   - ☐ I'd get angry and accuse him of hiding something
   - ☐ other ______________________________

4. If your fiancé wanted to know details of your previous relationships, would you be willing to tell him?
   - ☐ yes
   - ☐ yes, generally
   - ☐ I wouldn't want to be bothered going into detail
   - ☐ I'd rather not; it's embarrassing
   - ☐ I'd rather not; I don't want to upset him
   - ☐ no, it's in the past
   - ☐ no, it's private

Reading Tip

After you've finished a chapter (or the whole book), compare your answers with your fiancé's. For more reading tips, see the Introduction.

5. Were you ever abused in a previous relationship?
   - ☐ yes, I was physically abused (e.g. beaten, raped)
   - ☐ yes, I was emotionally abused
   - ☐ yes, I was threatened with harm
   - ☐ no, I was never abused in any of my relationships

6. Would you ever mentally compare your husband's personality or body to those of a previous boyfriend?
   - ☐ definitely
   - ☐ probably
   - ☐ I'd try not to
   - ☐ I wouldn't

7. Would you ever tell your husband how he compares to a past boyfriend?
   - ☐ yes
   - ☐ no
   - ☐ I might if I was angry and trying to hurt him with an unfavorable comparison
   - ☐ I might tell him if it was a favorable comparison
   - ☐ yes, I'd tell him if it was a favorable comparison

Conclusion

We (the authors) firmly believe that the best way to prevent divorce is to get to know each other well before you get married. If you are in a counseling program, this book complements what is covered. If you are not, this book by itself will help you to discover your issues.

What's the first step toward a happy marriage? First, find out where you disagree with your fiancé. Then, assess each of those issues to determine which ones you are flexible on and which ones are truly important to you—the ones that are basic to your view of a happy marriage.

To do this step, you need to look again at the questions that you answered differently. Mark those that are really important to you with a *. These will be the "make or break" issues. You will probably mark different questions than your fiancé—but if either one of you says it's important, it has to become important to both of you. And you need to resolve all these important issues before you get married.

Some people might find that they only have one or two "make or break" issues and think that they don't need to worry. If that describes you, you must realize that many marriages have broken up over just one unresolved "make or break" issue. Get it resolved!

To help you with this process, we have provided a scoring system on the book's web site, www.knowingme-knowingyou.com. It helps you to keep track of the number of questions that are potential "hot spots" in your relationship.

We hope that you have found this quiz helpful. Feel free to comment on the book at www.knowingme-knowingyou.com. May the work you put into your marriage lead to a lifetime of love.